THE PSYCHOGRAM

A History of an Asylum Newspaper

NATHANIEL M. SULLIVAN

HERITAGE BOOKS
2021

HERITAGE BOOKS

AN IMPRINT OF HERITAGE BOOKS, INC.

Books, CDs, and more—Worldwide

For our listing of thousands of titles see our website
at
www.HeritageBooks.com

Published 2021 by
HERITAGE BOOKS, INC.
Publishing Division
5810 Ruatan Street
Berwyn Heights, Md. 20740

International Standard Book Number
Paperbound: 978-0-7884-1202-8

To my mother, who instilled in me the love of reading.

ACKNOWLEDGMENTS

I would like to thank Daniel Myers and Maryclare Myers of the Morris Plains Museum, without whom I would not have learned about *The Psychogram* and been inspired to write this text.

Thanks to Frank Rybasack and Olin "Butch" Acker for allowing me to interview them regarding their childhood experiences growing up as children of the institution's police and fire chiefs. I would also like to thank Carole Golcher, who worked at Greystone assisting in the occupational therapy program.

Thank you James Lewis and the staff of the North Jersey History and Genealogy Center at the Morristown and Morris Township Library.

Thank you to Timothy Hacsi of the University of Massachusetts, Boston, for all of your help revising my text and helping me to terminate "would" from my vocabulary. Thank you to Elizabeth McCahill, Benjamin Johnson, and Olivia Weisser of the University of Massachusetts, Boston, for your help proofreading and providing me with guidance as I navigated this more obscure area of history looking for sources. A special thanks to Brian Regal, of Kean University, for your support and guidance, as well as for sparking my interest in the history of science and medicine as an undergraduate student.

Also, a big thanks to my friend and fellow teacher Jessica Duran, for taking the time to proofread my text while also trying to lesson plan during a pandemic.

TABLE OF CONTENTS

LIST OF IMAGES

CHAPTER 1

INTRODUCTION

In *Madness and Civilization,* Michel Foucault remarked that "confinement hid away unreason, and betrayed the shame it aroused; but it explicitly drew attention to madness, pointed to it."[1] Foucault believed that as American and European societies constructed incredible institutions of dramatic size and scope they also built mental walls to people who were increasingly ostracized from their communities. For more than a century, individuals living with mental disabilities led lives of indifference and without consequence inside the walls of almshouses and asylums. In the Progressive Era the treatment of the mentally ill changed and become more individualized. Slowly, mental institutions opened up to public scrutiny. One of the most unique methods in which the public learned about how these institutions functioned and the

---

[1] Foucault, Michel. *Madness and Civilization: a History of Insanity in the Age of Reason.* New York, NY: Vintage Books, 1988, 70.

1

care they provided was through the publication of hospital newsletters and magazines.

In the second half of the 19th century the construction of mental institutions in the United States was at its peak. With the realization that patients were going to be institutionalized for extended periods of time, most states began to erect large-scale facilities to accommodate this rapidly growing need. Gerald Grob notes that by 1880, "there were almost 140 public and private mental hospitals caring for nearly 41,000 patients." The majority of patients institutionalized were in public hospitals.[2] Greystone Park Psychiatric Hospital was constructed during this tumultuous time. Located in Morris Plains, New Jersey, Greystone opened its doors in 1876. It was located upon 740 acres of "ornately appointed hospital and beautifully landscaped property" that quickly became an attraction that garnered public attention.[3] One of the major turning points in Greystone's history would be the arrival of Dr. Britton Duroc Evans as Medical Director on June 1st,

---

[2] Grob, Gerald N. *Mental Illness and American Society: 1875-1940*. Princeton, NJ: Princeton University Press, 1983, 4.
[3] Tagliareni, Rusty, and Christina Mathews. *Greystone Park Psychiatric Hospital*. Charleston, SC: Arcadia Publishing, 2016, 18.

2

1892. His tenure as Medical Director lasted until his death in 1920. This is not a study of all mental hospitals in this era, or even a full study of Greystone, but instead is focusing on an unusual publication that provides insight into the lives of patients at Greystone.

The Psychogram was the jewel of Greystone Park Psychiatric Hospital's occupational therapy program, which began under Dr. Britton Duroc Evans and ran from 1916-1977. Housed in the Industrial Building on the hospital campus, patients, guided by hospital personnel, printed, bound, and distributed the newsletter to staff, as well as shipped issues to subscribers in the surrounding area of Morris Plains, New Jersey. Giving patients the outlet to voice their insight into the workings of the hospital, as well as their treatment, was an innovative and rewarding therapeutic process which was rooted in the progressive values of that time. In addition, it helped bring attention to the public about what an institution had to offer for those suffering from mental disabilities when most individuals afflicted were either hidden away or ostracized. Lastly, the production of a hospital newsletter

3

helped to bond patients and staff, in turn developing a mutual understanding for one another.

Hospital Newsletters and Magazines

In *Essays on the Social Situation of Mental Patients and Other Inmates*, Erving Goffman reflects that hospital magazines helped to bond staff and patients together. He notes that a newspaper or magazine was the "house organ" of an institution, in which "the printed content is such as to draw a circle around the institution and to give the accent of public reality to the world within."[4] Goffman provided an overview of the framework in which early hospital periodicals followed. The first kind of material covered was local promotions, trips and deaths. The second material was editorials. Editorials consisted of news from the outside world, essays, short stories, and poetry. Goffman notes that hospital periodicals survive in "the delicacy of a nice balance" in which "the staff allows itself to be interviewed, written about, and read about by inmates, thus coming under some slight control of the writers and readers; at the same time, inmates are given an

---

[4] Goffman, Erving, *Asylums: Essays on the Social Situation of Mental Patients and Other Inmates* (New York, NY: Anchor, 1961).

4

opportunity to show that they are high enough on the human scale to handle the official language and official line with educated competence."[5]

Hospital magazines and newsletters, such as *The Psychogram,* can be viewed as one of the progressive attempts at individualized care and innovative treatment of patients with mental disabilities. Pauline Prior and Gillian McClelland in *Through the Lens of the Hospital Magazine* analyze two hospital's magazines that were published in Belfast in the 1960s and 1970s. The *Speedwell* from Holywell Hospital, Antrim, and *The Sketch* from Downshire Hospital, Downpatrick were an essential part of therapy for patients with mental disabilities. Prior and McClelland argue that hospital magazines gave patients opportunities to express their views on life in the hospital and helped mental institutions promote the ethos of a therapeutic community.[6]

With *Speedwell* the goal of the medical superintendent in its creation was to "establish a therapeutic community within the hospital. It aimed to appeal to patients, staff, their friends, and any

---

[5] Ibid.
[6] Prior, Pauline, and Gillian McClelland. "Through the Lens of the Hospital Magazine: Downshire and Holywell Psychiatric Hospitals in the 1960s and 1970s." *History of Psychiatry* 24, no. 4 (2013): 399–414, 400-401.

5

other persons interested in the life of the hospital." *Speedwell*, unlike *The Psychogram*, was primarily dominated by the hospital staff, although it did accept patient contributions. There were sections which included event calendars, artwork, holidays, editorials, and articles related to mental hygiene. *The Sketch* was part of Downshire Hospital's occupational therapy department and was overseen by staff, but edited and printed by the patients. This magazine included content such as articles, letters, poems, and artwork by patients.[7]

Institutionalization as Treatment

The most drastic change that occurred in the treatment of the mentally ill in the United States was the shifting of those with mental disabilities from a communal, collective environment of care into a confined, structured institution led by medical professionals. The current historiography of mental healthcare focuses primarily on the institutional period from the late nineteenth century into the period of deinstitutionalization in the late twentieth century. There is also a growing field of medical

---

[7] Ibid.

historians that is beginning to look back at the issue of societal treatment of the mentally ill in the early modern period and how and why communities and progressive leaders felt that institutionalization was the best route of treatment.

Historian Gerald Grob was known as the preeminent authority on the history of mental healthcare in the United States. In *The Mad Among Us,* Grob notes that in Colonial America mental illness was viewed by society as more of a social and economic issue, rather than medical. Those with mental illnesses were commonly referred to in texts as "distracted" or "idiots." Rarely were treatments or therapies mentioned before the nineteenth century. During this time it was common to believe that mental disabilities came from not just natural, but supernatural, origins.[8]

In *Mental Illness in American Society 1875-1940,* Grob argues that the major change that came to treating the mentally ill was due to the increasing populations of cities in the United States. In rural communities the caretaker of the mentally ill was the family and community. As immigration drastically increased to the United

---

[8] Grob, Gerald N. *Mad Among Us*. Riverside: Free Press, 2011, 6-8.

States from 1830 to 1850 into the cities, so did those that had not

received care in their countries of origin. The response was

institutionalization. As more Americans went to work during this

emerging period of industrialization they looked to public

institutions to care for the mentally ill. Two of the lead activists

campaigning for mental health in the nineteenth century were

Dorothea Dix and Horace Mann. A major change which had

lasting implications for mental hospitals was the changing

demographics of the populations. Originally, the focus was on

treating patients that were young to middle aged for short periods,

however "after 1900 the proportion of aged senile persons residing

in hospitals increased sharply, thus altering the functions of an

institution that had been designed for quite different purposes." [9]

In the 1991 article *The Political Economy of Madness:*

The Expansion of the Asylum in Progressive America, historian

John Sutton builds upon Grob's thesis that asylums were forced to

absorb increasing numbers of the elderly and poor who could no

longer be confined to almshouses. Sutton argues that the

expansion of asylums was a product of organizational and political

---

[9] Grob, Gerald N. *Mental Illness and American Society: 1875-1940*. Princeton, NJ: Princeton University Press, 1983, 4-5.

forces rather than an increase in insanity. A result was the divergence of mental health techniques provided by hospitals, with drastically different approaches developing. Sutton argues that doctors were given authority to define appropriate psychiatric practices at their hospitals, which included "haphazard experimentation with a number of invasive somatic therapies, including physical restraints, cold baths, tooth extractions, and surgery on the brain and genitals. These cruel and useless treatments encouraged the professional tendency to blur the line between insanity and physical disorder – and thereby further weakened the asylum's ability to define a clear domain of action."[10]

David Gollaher in *Voice for the Mad* states that Dorothea Dix "sponsored and drafted legislation, built major institutions around the country, directed the Civil War army nurses, and forced her countrymen to confront one of the nation's ugliest and most perplexing social problems." Gollaher notes that Dix did not create the asylum system in America, however she brought the issue of

---

[10] Sutton, John R. "The Political Economy of Madness: The Expansion of the Asylum in Progressive America." *American Sociological Review* 56, no. 5 (1991): 668.

mental illness and homelessness to the forefront of public policy.

Dix was a leader for the emerging progressive movement, arguing

that it was the responsibility of the state to provide for those who

could not care for themselves. Unfortunately, Gollaher remarks,

Dix has "remained famous, yet unknown." He suggests that since

her identity was tied to the development and spread of the asylum

system, her achievements have fallen alongside their

dismantlement.[11]

Historian and philosopher Michel Foucault in *Madness*

and Civilization analyzes how Europe viewed the mentally ill as

early as the Middle Ages. He argues that in the past the mentally

ill were not as ostracized by society as they were in the eighteenth

century and thereafter. Both Grob and Foucault state that prior to

industrialization, the mentally ill were not shunned by society, but

seen as part of their local communities. The major change,

according to Foucault, was designating the mentally ill as an

"other," thus carrying a societal stigma that carries into the present

day.[12]

---

[11] Gollaher, David. *Voice for the Mad: The Life of Dorothea Dix*. New York: Free Press, 1995.
[12] Foucault, Michel. *Madness and Civilization: a History of Insanity in the Age of Reason*. New York, NY: Vintage Books, 1988.

The classification of the "other" was heightened with the construction and implementation of the asylum system in the eighteenth and nineteenth centuries. Foucault noted that the eighteenth century "linked madness more firmly than ever to confinement," which in turn caused more alienation from families and the communities where they were raised.[13] Patients were treated like animals, with misbehavior only to be "corrected" by physical abuse. Foucault comments that "unchained animality could be mastered only by discipline and brutalizing," that the "animality of madness was tamed only by such discipline whose meaning was not to raise the bestial to the human, but to restore man to what was purely animal within him."[14] In order to maintain social control the asylum system was organized so that the patients could recognize that they were being observed at all times, and that if they disobeyed authority there would be condemnation.

In *Conscience and Convenience*, David Rothman argues that progressive reforms in the late nineteenth century did not significantly improve inherited practices in treating mental illness.

---

[13] Foucault, Michel. *Madness and Civilization: a History of Insanity in the Age of Reason*. New York, NY: Vintage Books, 1988, 227.
[14] Foucault, Michel. *Madness and Civilization: a History of Insanity in the Age of Reason*. New York, NY: Vintage Books, 1988, 75.

In contrast to the Jacksonian philosophy, the progressives wanted to individualize care. They were convinced that "their innovations could satisfy all goals." Rothman reflected that progressives believed that "the same person in the same institution could at once guard and help, protect and rehabilitate, maintain custody and deliver treatment."[15]

As the number of patients increased, the goal of individualizing treatment became progressively more difficult for many institutions. Neglect was rampant. In addition, mental institutions became long term care facilities, in contrast to their original intent of curing and releasing patients back into society. Rothman notes that "custodial care was generally not humane care" and that "substandard institutional conditions came to be accepted as something less than scandalous," especially when many of the patients were foreign-born.[16]

Historian Katherine Anderson in *Behind the Walls: Hidden Histories* chronicles the histories of the development of the asylum system in New England. She argues that the

_____

[15] Rothman, David J. *Conscience and Convenience: the Asylum and Its Alternatives in Progressive America*. Routledge, 2017, 10.
[16] Ibid, 2017, 21, 24.

development of the asylum system was inevitable. Communities that began to experience the growing burden of mental illness that came with increased populations turned to almshouses for assistance. Many of these locations were temporary and a large-scale system was needed to assist these individuals that suffered not just from mental illness, but homelessness, as well as alcoholism and other various diseases. Like Gollaher, Anderson notes that major change did not happen in this region until the arrival of Dorothea Dix. Dix witnessed in Massachusetts how the mentally ill were being treated; many were imprisoned and viewed as incurable rabid animals. This experience is what Anderson argues sparked Dix to begin her crusade for the mentally ill.[17]

In contrast to Anderson, Rothman argues that asylums were by no means superior to almshouses. He argued in *Conscience and Convenience* that "asylums still relied upon restraints, perhaps reluctantly, but nevertheless frequently," and that "boards of managers charged to oversee institutions were

---

[17] Anderson, Katherine. *Behind the Walls: Hidden Histories*, 2013, 8.

useless."[18] While historians such as Rothman could find no value in large-scale institutionalization, others saw that this progressive approach could enable patients to discover a sense of self-worth and new outlets to express themselves.

Benjamin Reiss in *Theaters of Madness* contends that the large-scale asylums that were created in the nineteenth century became their own self-contained cultural ecosystems, which produced works of art and influenced the world outside their walls. Throughout his text he reflects on the cultural components of patient life within asylum walls, that inside could be found "debating societies, lectures series, literary journals for patients, daguerreotype workshops, and fairs. Patients were taught in schools, preached to in chapels, encouraged to participate in dramatic groups, and coached in the arts of polite society." He argues that "asylums became at once laboratories for purifying the national culture and theaters where this could be observed."[19]

Nurse and historian Shirley Smoyak in her editorial piece *What's New is Really Old* in the *Journal of Psychosocial Nursing*

---

[18] Rothman, David J. *Conscience and Convenience: the Asylum and Its Alternatives in Progressive America*. Routledge, 2017, 296.
[19] Reiss, Benjamin. *Theaters of Madness*. Chicago: University of Chicago Press, 2008, XVII.

analyzes hospital mission statements from the nineteenth century,

including that of Greystone, and reflects that many of the best

practices used today are rooted in foundational principals

developed in the past. Some of these new directions in patient care

include "total respect for patients, staff awareness of their own

personal issues and professional beliefs, patient involvement in

their treatment planning and interventions, assurance of a least-

restrictive environment, no use of physical or chemical restraints,

and care delivery based on best practices derived from scientific

evidence.[20]

---

[20] Smoyak, Shirley A. "What's New Is Really Old." *Journal of Psychosocial Nursing* 45, no. 10, 2007, 8.

Conclusion

 The Psychogram encompasses the progressive values of the time in which the individualization of treatment was at the forefront of the movement and mental institutions aimed to portray themselves as centers of innovation. The newsletter gave readers unique insight into the daily workings of a mental institution in the early twentieth century from the perspective of patients and staff.

 The Psychogram is a prime example of an institution trying to individualize care. Patients in occupational programs at Greystone, such as in the print shop had the freedom to explore their self-identity in a way that many institutions at the time did not allow. Patients wrote poems, articles, and had letters published within the newsletter that gave them the opportunity to express themselves to the hospital community and public.

 Grob notes that during this time in the early twentieth century, "a consensus emerged on the need to define a new relationship between community and hospital."[21] *The Psychogram* bridged that relationship as it allowed patients and medical staff to communicate with the world outside the hospital walls. It gave a

---

[21] Grob, Gerald N. *Mental Illness and American Society: 1875-1940*. Princeton, NJ: Princeton University Press, 1983, 236.

face to the psychiatric patient, rather than a number. In addition, working in an area such as the print shop helped patients to develop valuable skills that allowed them to pursue employment and fulfilling lives once discharged.

CHAPTER 2

GREYSTONE PARK

The treatment and care of those with mental disabilities

was redefined in the late 19th century. As cities grew in population,

so did the visibility of the mentally disabled. Although in rural

sections of the country care was family and community-based,

cities looked to the construction of hospitals of incredible size and

scale to provide medical care and residence. According to Gerald

Grob, the "growing exclusiveness of private hospitals became a

widespread phenomenon and included institutions founded later in

the century."[22] Most local communities were not willing to pay the

costs of treating the residents. This, Grob notes, lead to the

formation of an institutionally oriented mental health policy,

which was laid in the Northeast. He reflects that the "founding of a

state asylum in Massachusetts in 1830 acted as a catalyst that set

in motion a movement designed to make state hospitals the focal

point of mental health policy."[23] Greystone Park was a key public

---

[22] Grob, Gerald N. *Mad Among Us*. Riverside: Free Press, 2011, 38.
[23] Ibid, 43.

state institution founded to provide residents with mental disabilities a safe haven and innovative options for treatment, while others were combating internal strife.

Greystone Park Psychiatric Hospital was constructed in 1876 in order to help the state of New Jersey cope with the overcrowded conditions found in Trenton. The hospital early on implemented innovative forms of treatment, such as occupational therapy. With the arrival of Dr. Britton Duroc Evans in 1892 as the new Medical Director, the institution was overhauled with the construction of numerous buildings for both staff and patient care. In addition, a more systematic and expansive approach for occupational therapy was implemented. One of the foundational components of Evans' philosophy of treatment, which he embedded in the framework of the hospital, was putting patients to work. This was encapsulated in the establishment of *The Psychogram* newsletter in 1916.[24]

---

[24] Evans, Britton D. *Why We Exist.* The Psychogram (Morris Plains), August 1916, 6.

Issues at Trenton

The need for a second mental hospital in New Jersey grew rapidly every year in the mid nineteenth century. The New Jersey State Lunatic Asylum, later known as Trenton Psychiatric Hospital, had been the sole state-run mental hospital in New Jersey since its founding in 1848 by Dorothea Dix. According to the *Newark Daily Advertiser,* Trenton was designed and built at a time when there were about twenty mental hospitals in the United States in total. Eight of those were private institutions and fourteen states at that time did not even have a psychiatric institution of any kind. Those individuals that had mental afflictions became public charges, being placed in poorhouses or eventually ending up in jails.[25]

Even after the creation of large state-ran mental institutions, most of the mentally ill were still sent to poorhouses. Michael Katz notes that "although Dix's indefatigable campaigns within several states had promoted the creation of state mental hospitals, these new institutions could not accommodate a majority of those in need of care. In larger states, poorhouses near

---

[25] "The State and Its Insane." *Newark Daily Advertiser*. December 7, 1894.

20

cities often had separate departments for the mentally ill or separate hospitals for the insane poor. But in more rural areas, the mentally ill remained in almshouses, mixed with the other inmates, receiving little if any special treatment."[26] Most criticism was placed on the cost of establishing and running these massive institutions. One of the early state-run asylums was the Willard Asylum for the Insane, which opened in 1869 in New York. Katz reflects that "when Willard opened, there were 1,500 insane people in county care in New York State; six years later Willard was full and 1,300 mentally ill people still remained in county institutions."[27] New York was not alone in trying to keep up with the demand of providing care for an ever-increasing population of mentally ill.

In the 1876 Annual Report of the Managers and Officers of the New Jersey State Lunatic Asylum at Trenton, the situation regarding living conditions was described as continuing to decline, even with attempts by administration to construct additional accommodations. Secretary Thomas Stryker reflected that "there

---

[26] Katz, Michael B. *In the Shadow of the Poorhouse a Social History of Welfare in America*. New York: BasicBooks, 1998, 102.
[27] Ibid, 103.

are now in the Asylum nearly three hundred patients more than the building is designed to accommodate, and the applications for admission continue to increase rather than to diminish."[28] Due to the overwhelming numbers of patients the Superintendent of the institution was instructed by the Board of Managers to refuse all applications for the admission of new patients until a solution could be found.[29]

Trenton's asylum gained notoriety for many of the wrong reasons, a problem that continued into the 20th century. Andrew Scull in his text *Madhouse* reflects on one of its most infamous staff members, Medical Director Henry Cotton. Cotton earned the nickname of the "mad doctor" during his time at the hospital from 1907 to 1930.[30] He believed that mental illnesses were caused by infections, and in accordance with this stance he conducted hundreds of experimental surgeries, including on his own children. Scull tells of a hospital where there were "stories of patients being beaten, kicked, and dragged screaming into the operating room, of

---

[28] Stryker, Thomas J. "*1876 Annual Report of the Managers and Officers of the New Jersey State Lunatic Asylum at Trenton*" (Trenton, 1876), 7.
[29] Ibid
[30] Scull, Andrew. *Madhouse: A Tragic Tale of Megalomania and Modern Medicine*. New Haven, Conn: Yale University Press, 2007, 6.

trolleys filled with body parts and not a few corpses streaming in

the opposite direction(…)."[31] As time went on the hospital grew in

size and faced the fate many of its fellow institutions had to

contend with, the issue of overcrowding and diminishing state

funding. In addition, the hospital began to admit patients that were

convicted of criminal charges. This was a cause for alarm for

many families that had relatives residing in the hospital.[32]

[31] Scull, Andrew. *Madhouse: A Tragic Tale of Megalomania and Modern Medicine*. New Haven, Conn: Yale University Press, 2007, 2.
[32] Stryker, Thomas J. "*1876 Annual Report of the Managers and Officers of the New Jersey State Lunatic Asylum at Trenton*" (Trenton, 1876), 8.

Image 1: Medical Director Dr. Briton Duroc Evans. (Photo courtesy of the Morris Plains Museum)

Due to the overcrowding, which in turn lead to an increase in violence that had plagued the hospital for years, Governor Randolph in 1871 appointed a commission to select a property to use for the state's second mental hospital. The commissioners consisted of Hon. George Vail, Samuel Lillie, MD., Beach Vanderpool, Anthony Reckless, George A. Halsey, William G. Lathrop, and John S. Read. Under the guidance of superintendents of construction appointed by the governor work on the hospital pushed forward rapidly.[33]

After several changes in leadership during the planning stage, Dr. H. A. Buttolph was appointed the sole superintendent of the developing location for the new asylum at Morris Plains. Prior to his arrival Buttolph was Medical Superintendent at Trenton. The hospital was known by a series of different names over its history, from the State Asylum for the Insane at Morristown, the New Jersey State Hospital at Morris Plains, and finally Greystone Park Psychiatric Hospital in 1924.[34] Buttolph headed Greystone for eight years until he resigned after the introduction by the state of the dual-management system in 1885. Under the dual-management system the hospital's top administration position of the superintendent was split into that of the medical director and a warden, both of whom reported directly to the Board of Managers. According to the November 1916 issue of *The Psychogram*, the change was made because it was found by the board of managers

---

[33] Evans, Britton D. "History of the New Jersey State Hospital at Morris Plains" *The Psychogram* (Morris Plains), November 1916, 4.
[34] "Time Line." Preserve Greystone - History of Greystone Park Psychiatric Hospital. http://preservegreystone.org/history.html.

that "the number of patients is so large that the Superintendent could not attend to his medical duties and also have the general supervision and control of business matters of the asylum."[35]

The first work done during construction was the building of the railroad branch from Morris Plains to the rear of the hospital site. This was vital for the transportation of supplies and workers. The hospital's central building was completed in a period of five years. During construction there were as many as eighteen hundred men employed at a time. Close to 3 million dollars went towards construction, which included the purchasing of grounds, furnishing administration living rooms, offices, and wards. Some buildings that were on the property at the time of purchase were repurposed, such as the slaughterhouse. It was changed into a brush factory. It was powered by a nearby brook that passed the building. The hospital began receiving patients from Trenton on August 17, 1876 when 292 patients were transferred. According to Dr. E. More Fisher in 1916, the hospital was not always as

---

[35] Evans, Britton D. "History of the New Jersey State Hospital at Morris Plains" *The Psychogram* (Morris Plains), November 1916, 4.

efficient as it eventually become, that it had improved from a "state of crudity" to a "present condition of completeness."[36]

The Arrival of Doctor Evans

Britton Duroc Evans was born in Caroline Country, Maryland on October 1, 1858. His parents were Louis and Lucinda Boone Evans. His father, Louis Evans, was also a physician and practiced medicine in Maryland. Louis attended two medical schools in Philadelphia and practiced in the city early in his career. He later returned to Maryland where he met Lucina Boone. Britton Duroc Evans was raised with his four sisters and four brothers, all within an academic environment. He was named after his grandfather, Britton Evans, who served in several military engagements. Most notably, the first Britton Evans was a lieutenant of artillery in the War of 1812. He also fought in the battle of River Raisin, as well as the Second Seminole War. According to the *Biographical and Genealogical History of Morris County*, at the time of his death, Britton Evans, "was organizing a company to go to Greece to help her in her struggle for independence, against Turkey. His original

[36] Fisher, E. Moore "History of the New Jersey State Hospital at Morris Plains" The Psychogram (Morris Plains), October 1916, 3.

commission, signed by President Monroe and Madison, and also the original credentials which enabled him to organize a company of aid of the Greeks, are in possession of his grandson, Dr. Evans, of Morris Plains." Three of his sons became physicians.[37]

Following in the footsteps of his father, Britton Duroc Evans studied medicine at the College of Physicians and Surgeons in Baltimore. In 1885 he graduated and practiced medicine for 2 years in Kent, Maryland. Following his time in Kent, Evans was elected Assistant Physician to the Maryland Hospital for the Insane, where he worked for five years. His first administrative position was Medical Superintendent of the Maryland Institution for Feeble Minded, however "he was in charge of this place only a short time, as his reputation had become so widely known that he was elected by the Board of Managers of the New Jersey State Hospital for the Insane at Morris Plains to become Medical Director." His first day as Medical Director was on June 1st, 1892.[38]

---

[37] Biographical and Genealogical History of Morris County, New Jersey, Volume I, the Lewis Publishing Company, New York and Chicago, 1899.
[38] "The N.J. State Hospital. Something About This Great Institution at Morris Plains - B. D. Evans, Medical Director." *The Journal*, November 1894.

The issue of overcrowding that Trenton and other public mental asylums faced was compounded by the increasing use of institutions to house prisoners. In 1902, Medical Director Evans of Greystone Park alerted the public of this internal threat. In his 1902 Annual Report, Evans demanded that convicts should be separated from the general patient population immediately. He remarked that "year after year I have in the annual reports called attention to the many evils arising out of keeping this class among patients whose lives are free from criminality. To those patients who realize that in their affliction and loss of liberty they are kept in the same building with convicts of the vilest sort, the effect is to bring about feelings of dissatisfaction, humiliation and resentment, and in many instances improvement and recovery are retarded if not made impossible."[39]

Dr. Evans believed that occupational therapy as a form of treatment was a necessity for recovery. He was critical of the stagnancy regarding the treatment of the mentally ill that he observed in several states. On January 1916, towards the end of

---

[39] Evans, Britton D. "*Annual Report of the Board of Managers of the New Jersey State Hospital at Morristown for the Year ending in October 31, 1902*" (Morris Plains), 20.

his career, Evans presented at a symposium in Spring Lake, New

Jersey for the 149th Annual Meeting of the Medical Society of

New Jersey.

He remarked that:

> The fact still remains that hospitals are necessary for the
> intelligent and humane treatment of persons afflicted with
> insanity and that such institutions should be so constructed
> and conducted as to give the highest order of efficiency in
> the treatment, care and prevention of medical disorders
> and give a substantial protection to the rights of the citizen
> alleged to be insane, promote the integrity of society,
> decrease hereditary taint and provide safe keeping for such
> as are a menace to public safety, with due consideration
> for the principles of economy, justice and laws of
> humanity.[40]

This standard of treatment endured during his tenure as Medical

Director, as well as with his successor, Marcus Curry.

---

[40] Evans, Britton D. "Institutional Care of the Insane." *Journal of The Medical Society of New Jersey* XIII, no. 1 (January 1916): 1–6, 3

Occupational Therapy at Greystone

Under Evans, Greystone had one of the largest occupational therapy programs in the state. The hospital was almost entirely self-sufficient. Their occupational program originally started as a form of diversional occupation. According to Dr. Frank Mikels, a pathologist and junior assistant physician at the hospital, diversional occupation was "any form of human activity which may be prescribed for the purpose of diverting the minds of the patients from their morbid ideas to the attention of wholesome and entertaining pursuits."[41] These activities were very extensive in range and, according to Mikels, could be nearly anything that the human being is capable of at work or play. He notes that it is a therapeutic measure that can be used as a "curative measure." Thanks to the successful petitioning for additional funding to the state, Evans expanded every year the number of options patients had to entertain themselves with, as well as develop skills that could be utilized once they have left the hospital.

---

[41] Mikels, Frank M. "Diversional Occupation for Patients." *The Psychogram* (Morris Plains), November 1916, Vol. 1 ed., No. 5, 5.

The earliest form of occupational therapy at Greystone was farming the surrounding land of the hospital complex. Farm work was implemented since the establishment of the hospital. Indoor work consisted of assisting in the dining rooms and keeping the corridors clean. Mikels reflected in 1916 that before the construction of the Industrial Building it was difficult to get patients to engage in outdoor work, as many prior to their arrival were merchants, attorneys, physicians, and engineers. They viewed farming and maintaining the hospital grounds as "common work."[42]

Funding from the state dramatically increased during Evans' time as Medical Director from 1892-1920. The Annual Report of 1892 records that for that year the hospital received $16,067 for convict patients and $39,958 for county patients from the State Treasurer.[43] His first year at the hospital Evans wasted no time making structural improvements, such as

> in the ducts and rooms connecting with the kitchen, by laying three thousand nine hundred and thirty-eight square feet of cement floor, of the best quality, to replace plank;

---

[42] Mikels, Frank M. "Diversional Occupation for Patients." *The Psychogram* (Morris Plains), November 1916, Vol. 1 ed., No. 5, 5.
[43] Evans, Britton D. *"Annual Report of the Board of Managers of the New Jersey State Hospital at Morristown for the Year ending in October 31, 1892"* (Trenton, 1894), 47.

the in boiler-house, by arranging the steam main connecting with the boilers so the pressure could be made either high, to use in furnishing motive power, or low, for heating purposes. This is estimated to save 15 percent of the coal necessary for the latter purpose, amounting in one year to a saving of about six hundred dollars.[44]

By 1918 the Annual Report records an increase in state

funding for patients. The

hospital received $124,563.55 for county patients and $160,795.27

for state indigent.[45] Evans noted that even at that point in time,

more assistance was needed from the state. Not just of funds, but

of materials for the occupational therapy program. He recorded

that "After days or months of patient instruction, an inmate is

taught some line of work; true it may be done in a mechanical

way, but it is done, and fairly satisfactorily; then, though ordered,

the necessary material is not at hand for a continuance of this line

of endeavor. The result is heart racking to those who have devoted

their time and energy to teaching the patient."[46] In the print shop

alone at the hospital "166 jobs have been done, requiring 306,000

---

[44] Ibid, 50.

[45] Evans, Britton D. "*Annual Report of the Board of Managers of the New Jersey State Hospital at Morristown For the Period From November 1st 1917 to June 30th 1918*" (Hospital Print, 1919), 67.

[46] Evans, Britton D. "*Annual Report of the Board of Managers of the New Jersey State Hospital at Morristown For the Period From November 1st 1917 to June 30th 1918*" (Hospital Print, 1919), 19.

impressions. To these may be added 61,000 for annual report of 1917 and 112,800 for issues of *The Psychogram*. The number of forms ruled was 120.[47]

Medical Staff

B D Evans M.D.
Eliot Gorton M. D. Thomas P. Prout M.D.
Peter S. Mallon M. D. Arthur S. Corwin M D.

Image 2: Medical Director Britton Duroc Evans with Staff. Undated. (Photo Courtesy of the Morris Plains Museum)

The Industrial Building was the highlight of the occupational program at Greystone. It was equipped with the

_____

[47] Ibid, 20.

necessary tools for a print shop, bookbinding, to manufacture rugs, tapestry, as well as a variety of different arts and crafts. According to Dr. George R. Hampton, these changes made under Evans were viewed positively across the hospital by both the staff, as well as the patients. Hampton commented in the February 1917 edition of *The Psychogram* that "the old time chains and manacles have long since gone," that the "occupational method of treatment has been found to be very beneficial for the patients who are convalescing, and who are on a fair road to recovery."[48]

Image 3: The Industrial Building, 1914. (Annual Report, 1914, 13.)

---

[48] Hampton, George R. "Modern Care of the Insane." *The Psychogram* (Morris Plains), February 1917, 16.

In 1914 the Industrial Building was constructed in order to provide patients with a facility in order to be treated through the use of occupational therapy. In the 1914 Annual Report, Dr. Evans reflected on its completion that:

> There has been an awakening throughout the country relative to the industrial occupation of patients. No one familiar with the care and treatment of insane persons has entirely overlooked the fact that they should be, as far as possible, employed, but not enough thought has been given to providing a sufficiently diversified line of occupation.[49]

It was large in scale and could be viewed from many angles of the hospital campus, as the main building was structurally flat and contained numerous windows throughout for natural lighting. The printing and bookbinding area was located on the first floor of the building. The upper floor space was "given to carpet and towel weaving, raffia work, fancy and embroidery work of all kinds."[50] The selection of work opportunities at the hospital for patients was so extensive in scope that the Industrial Building was not large enough to accommodate all jobs. The dormitory building that Evans established a year earlier housed the areas for

---

[49] Evans, Britton D. *"Annual Report of the Board of Managers of the New Jersey State Hospital at Morristown for the Year ending in October 31, 1914"* (Trenton, 1894), 14.
[50] Ibid.

brush and broom making, chair caning, carpet weaving, and other forms of carpentry in its basement.[51]

Evans highlighted in his Annual Report how he believed that occupational therapy was to be the hospital's most important feature. He noted that:

> With the continued support of the Managers and substantial assistance from the Legislature there is no reason why industrial occupation shall not become not only the most important feature of our work, but a means of reducing the cost of maintenance and at the same time operate to beautify and make more pleasing the home life of those, who, because of disease, it is found necessary to place in this large institution.[52]

On February, 1917 there were 225 patients listed as being employed in the industrial department for several hours each day. Mikels noted that some of the patients follow similar jobs that they had prior to admission, while others were instructed to learn valuable skills and trades that they will need when they leave. He reflected that "patients, who are always restless and agitated if permitted to remain idle on the wards for weeks, can here be seen busily engaged in some useful occupation."[53] Instructors were

---

[51] Ibid, 17.
[52] Evans, Britton D. *"Annual Report of the Board of Managers of the New Jersey State Hospital at Morristown for the Year ending in October 31, 1914"* (Trenton, 1894), 14.
[53] Ibid.

readily available to help or assist any of the patients to maintain interest in their task at hand. What helped to garner the interest of the patients was having equipment that looked as similar to that of regular commercial grade machinery as possible. Once patients were able to view themselves as producers and that the therapy itself was not a treatment, but a job which they could relate to and deem respectable, the chances of participation increased.

Image 4: Occupational Therapy Department Vendors on Hospital Grounds

(Photo Courtesy of the Morris Plains Museum)

From May 11th, 1915 through the 14th, Evans and Mikels presented their research and system established used for occupational therapy to the Medico-Psychological Association at Old Point Comfort, Virginia. These lectures were published by the

American Journal of Insanity in an article titled *The Therapeutic and Economic Value of Diversional Occupation.*[54]

Before assigning a patient a position in the occupational therapy program each individual was carefully studied. This included their life prior to admission in order to verify that the therapy benefited their condition.[55] The safety of the patients that worked in the program was the most important priority for staff. The Industrial Building had many safety components in place that factories at the time did not have. Evans notes that any building for an occupational therapy program was required to be properly ventilated and illuminated, with modern safety devices in place in order to prevent accidents while patients manipulate the machinery. If a patient fell ill or was injured there was emergency equipment accessible. In addition, there was available space for a "retiring room" where patients could rest if they became anxious or fatigued.[56]

---

[54] Evans, Britton D., and Frank M. Mikels. "*The Therapeutic and Economic Value of Diversional Occupation.*" The American Journal of Insanity LXXII (1915)
[55] Ibid, 22.
[56] Ibid, 38.

Evans observed that:

> In the printing department and bookbinders the results
> have been constantly positive and the development of this
> industry has been very progressive, both from a medical
> and an economic standpoint. Patients who have been in
> this institution for a long time without having contributed
> anything toward their maintenance have been able to do
> an order of work in the printing department which, if
> justly evaluated, would be greatly in excess of actual cost
> of their maintenance.[57]

Greystone Park in the 1940s-50s

According to Olin Acker, who grew up on the grounds of

Greystone in the 1940s and 1950s while his father was the

institutional fire chief, men and women worked in separate

facilities. Each group, however, worked collaboratively with staff

and sold their products to the public. Each weekday for 8 hours the

public was allowed to enter the grounds of Greystone to purchase

items made from the various programs in the occupational therapy

department. Men sold a range of wares from brushes, brooms, and

baskets made from willows, to furniture, printed literature, as well

as food. Across from the firehouse women sold food and products

---

[57] Evans, Britton D. *"Annual Report of the Board of Managers of the New Jersey
State Hospital at Morristown for the Year ending in October 31, 1916"* (Trenton,
1894), 37.

made from sewing, knitting, lace, crocheting. All products were sold from their front storeroom.[58]

Frank Rybasack, retired sergeant and police officer at Morris Plains, recalled that most patients had "free walk of the grounds at Greystone." As his father was the Greystone Police Chief, Frank had many opportunities to walk with him throughout the wards and many buildings on the hospital grounds. His father was responsible for investigating problems with patients, employee thefts, assaults, as well as the smuggling in of drugs. Frank noted that without the help of the patients the hospital would not have been able to effectively function.[59]

One area in particular that Frank vividly remembered was that of the utility tunnels. Underneath the hospital grounds were a series of ducts, of two to three levels, that connected exterior buildings such a dorms and the occupational department buildings with that of the main building. The most accessible entryway to the tunnels was from the main building. Beneath the main building was a convenience store where patients were employed. A few

[58] Sullivan, Nathaniel. "Interview of Olin "Butch" Acker." 15 Dec. 2019.
[59] Sullivan, Nathaniel. "Interview of Frank Rybasack." 15 Dec. 2019.

parole patients and staff were responsible for delivering food and utilities through the ducts on the hospital's underground trolleys.[60]

Many patients followed an occupational schedule. If the patients in the occupational therapy program did not show up for work, then they were assumed to be attempting an escape. Many patients did attempt a daily escape, however they usually never made it any further than the restaurants and shopping areas of Morris Plains. Frank's father would occasionally receive calls from restaurants not far from the hospital that patients had ordered food, eaten, and then couldn't pay the bill and confessed to the server who they were. As Greystone did not have a standardized uniform aside from khaki pants and a casual shirt, patients could not always be immediately identified.[61]

---

[60] Ibid.
[61] Ibid.

According to Daniel Meyers of the Morris Plains Museum, not all patients were admitted involuntarily. Many checked themselves in for a specified period of time in order to treat drug or alcohol addiction.

Conclusion

In conclusion, Greystone Park was constructed in order to lessen the overcrowded conditions at Trenton. Dr. Britton Duroc Evans overhauled the occupational therapy program through the construction of new buildings, such as the men's and women's Industrial Buildings. In addition, he established a systematic approach to occupational therapy and introduced a popular program, like *The Psychogram* newsletter, printed within the hospital's print shop.

Having an expansive occupational therapy program, with unique subsets, such as *The Psychogram* changed the doctor-patient dynamic. Prior and McClelland argue that "the idea of a therapeutic community was based on assumptions of genuine communication and respect between patients and staff, a flattening of power differentials, and a movement away from the hierarchical structures of a hospital."[62] It enabled patients to work side-by-side with staff to create a product which would invoke pride and a valuable life-long skillset. The self-worth that occupational

---

[62] Prior, Pauline, and Gillian McClelland. "Through the Lens of the Hospital Magazine: Downshire and Holywell Psychiatric Hospitals in the 1960s and 1970s." *History of Psychiatry* 24, no. 4 (2013): 399–414, 402.

programs, such as a *The Psychogram* garnered among patients can

be read in their own words:

> Life has bruised me, has chastised me;
> Made me bear the hardest lot;
> Put its foot upon my neck;
> But my spirit, broke it not.   M.[63]

---

[63] M. *Untitled.* The Psychogram (Morris Plains), February 1917, 20.

CHAPTER 3

AN AERIAL COURTSHIP

The Psychogram newsletter was the cornerstone of the occupational therapy department at Greystone. It provided families and the community with articles related to the treatment of patients, as well as events they could attend. It provided readers with unique insight from patients regarding their treatment and experiences while at a psychiatric hospital in the 20th century. Lastly, it gave patients an outlet to channel their anxiety and depression through creative means, such as poetry and essays.

Under the guidance of Dr. Evans, the first issue of *The Psychogram* was published and distributed directly from the print shop at Greystone on July of 1916. The subscription price was 50 cents annually, or 10 cents per individual copy. In addition to the contributing patients, Dr. Evans is noted as the editor-in-chief, members of the medical staff as associate editors, A.L. Rudick is listed as both business manager and treasurer, and John L.

Anderson as the newsletter's circulation manager.[64]

Dr. Evans reflects in the August 1916 edition of the

Psychogram that the newsletter was published:

> chiefly for the purpose of arousing a spirit of congeniality
> among all those who are residents of this institution; to
> encourage intellectual and moral improvements in the
> personalities of all those who have occasion to read it; to
> bring cheer and gladness to patients who are separated
> from their friends and relatives; and for the purpose of
> giving reliable information to the friends, relatives and
> such members of the general public as may be interested
> in the conduct and welfare of this large public charity
> maintained at Morris Plains for the treatment and care of
> persons suffering from the various forms of mental
> derangement.[65]

The staff of *The Psychogram* wanted a variety of

contributors in order to avoid overusing those patients that were

employed in the print shop of the Industrial Building. A series of

incentives were established in order to garner the attention of

potential patients that could become contributors. These included

competitions for prizes for those that could write the best "short

story, the best poem, the best description of the hospital grounds,

---

[64] Evans, Britton D. The Psychogram (Morris Plains), August 1916, i.
[65] Evans, Britton D. *Why We Exist.* The Psychogram (Morris Plains), August 1916, 6.

the best story of the dances and entertainments and the best

accounts of the baseball games."[66]

Image 5: Bookbinding Department, 1919. (Photo courtesy of the Morris Plains Museum)

Contributions are noted as being received from patients

and published under a pseudonym of their choice or their initials.

Patients were creative in their use of pseudonyms, with some

writing under Julius Caesar, Napoleon Bonaparte, Ramses II and

"The Colonel." One patient assuming the name Prince Michael of

Saxony contributed several articles and works of poetry over the

next few years. Dr. Evans reflects in the first edition of *The*

Psychogram that "our publication is the printed result of the action

---

[66] Evans, Britton D. *Why We Exist.* The Psychogram (Morris Plains), August 1916, 6.

of minds, as minds are found in this institution. If it does this satisfactorily, we will be content. Doubtless, there will appear from time to time some weird expressions of thought which will not be deleted. Nearly all the work in the various departments will be done by patients."[67]

According to the 1917 Annual Report the print shop had done all the ruling and printing used in the institution with the help of the patients. During that year alone "250 jobs were done, which required 600,000 impressions; besides this the annual report, which needed 100,000 impressions, was printed here, and *The Psychogram*, of which twelve issues called for 192,000 impressions." Dr. Evans reflected that "*The Psychogram* has been the means of stimulating good literary work on the part of the patients and others, and has proven an important factor in the re-education of patients where mental condition seemed hopeless."[68] *The Psychogram* was reflective of the creative and intellectual

---

[67] Evans, Britton D. *Why We* Exist. The Psychogram (Morris Plains), July 1916, 6.
[68] Evans, Britton D. "*Annual Report of the Board of Managers of the New Jersey State Hospital at Morristown for the Year ending in October 31, 1917*" (Trenton, 1894), 35.

48

work that patients were capable at a time when many occupational programs consisted of manual labor.

As patient populations grew and many hospitals became short on staff, it became increasingly difficult to continue maintaining personalized patient care. According to Grob, a solution many hospitals found was to set up training schools for nurses. Previously, most nurses received "what amounted to on-the-job-training." After the establishment of training schools for nurses on hospital grounds, hospital superintendents hoped to retain these newly-certified healthcare workers, at a time when turnover rates were high. The first mental hospital training school for nurses first opened in 1882 at the McLean Hospital in Boston. Greystone's program would form and begin admitting applicants in 1894. Grob argues that nurses" served as links between the medical staff and patients."[69] As a result of specialized training, patients at Greystone received therapy and guidance by nurses that were trained at the hospital where they were employed. They were an essential part of making occupational programs, such as the construction of *The Psychogram* work.

---

[69] Grob, Gerald N. *Mental Illness and American Society: 1875-1940*. Princeton, NJ: Princeton University Press, 1983, 244.

The Psychogram Makes Headlines

After the first year of publication the magazine became a popular source of discussion at the institution amongst both staff and patients. Dr. Evans commented that "the interest of the patients in *The Psychogram* grows with each issue. Its stimulation has been a great power towards mental improvement, and the work done for it has helped many to regain a large amount of their mental poise."[70] While the magazine was certainly popular within the hospital confines, it was also beginning to get the notice of the local media.

On March 27, 1917 *The Psychogram* received the attention of the Central New Jersey Home News, which published an article entitled *State Hospital Inmates Enter Newspaper Field.* The Home News notes that the patients "do all the typographical and much of the editorial work."[71] In addition, they remark that some of the contributions to the newsletter have "been received from patients show real ability, and their work is an interesting

---

[70] Evans, Britton D. "*Annual Report of the Board of Managers of the New Jersey State Hospital at Morristown for the Year ending in October 31, 1918*" (Trenton, 1894), 20.
[71] "State Hospital Inmates Enter Newspaper Field." *The Central New Jersey Home News.* March 27, 1917.

commentary on the various phases of insanity which affect the patient only in certain of his faculties without injuring others."[72] Patients were delighted at the attention they received from the public. To boast about their newfound "fame" in several editions of the Psychogram they wrote articles under the title *What Others Think About Us*.

Several other publications praised both *The Psychogram* and its editors. The *Newark Evening News* on July 14th commented that "so far as known, this is the first time that an institution caring for the mentally diseased issues a magazine containing, among other material, contributions from the patients."[73] The Paterson Press-Guardian noted that "It is not only a beautiful specimen of the typographic art, but it is pathetically interesting from the fact that a large part of its literary contents are furnished by patient of the institution."[74]

---

[72] Ibid.
[73] The Colonel *What Others Think About Us*. The Psychogram (Morris Plains), August 1916, 13.
[74] Ibid.

The Therapeutic Value of the Psychogram

Not all of the articles within *The Psychogram* were of a prideful nature. Many were solemn and reflective. One article by "R.B.G." in the August 1916 edition entitled *An Aerial Courtship* is an emotional and encouraging poem in which the author divulges his feelings of loneliness, but tries to provide the reader with a sense of hope. He exclaims "The world is run both early and late, by very much love and a little hate. The first is a power, the last a menace. Heaven for the first, but the second a furnace."[75]

Many of the articles written within the early editions of *The Psychogram* are spiritual in nature and promote harmony with oneself, peers, as well as nature in order to progress towards a fulfilling future outside the institution. R.B.G. suggests that "we can make it a better place to live by giving more than we should take of the good things in life, thereby not causing strife, by doing unto others as if they were brothers."[76] At the bottom of this article the editor left a note that shortly after it was contributed the patient was taken home by his relatives.

---

[75] R.B.G. *An Aerial Courtship.* The Psychogram (Morris Plains), August 1916, 12.
[76] Ibid.

The element of doubt, as it is displayed in *An Aeriel Courtship*, was present within many articles and poems published in *The Psychogram*. As the patients were given the opportunity to contribute as well as edit, working on the newsletter enabled them to bond and establish a sense of community. In doing so many patients built upon one another's work and often their contributions were included adjoining each other. Directly after this article is a short poem in which author T.E.B. builds upon the sense of overwhelming doubt that inhibits R.B.G.'s text. Untitled, it reads as follows:

> Many a storm tossed and beaten vessel would have reached port if it hadn't been for that one long last wave of angry waters that overwhelmed them.
> Regrets are the principal weight that stretched many a hangman's rope.
> Remorse so resembles in its uselessness, a last year's bird, next that, well! What's the use?[77]

Although many patients had to face the stark reality that Greystone may be their home for the foreseeable future, having outlets such as the Psychogram and others within the occupational program provided them with a sense of self-worth, and a drive to move forward.

---

[77] T.E.B. The Psychogram (Morris Plains), August 1916, 12.

Working at an Asylum

Throughout every issue of *The Psychogram* patients expressed their appreciation for the staff at Greystone in providing them an outlet to contribute to the hospital and surrounding community of Morris Plains as part of their occupational therapy program. Although the Industrial Building was the center of the printing and distribution of The Psychogram, almost every aspect of the hospital grounds was utilized in one form or another to provide patients treatment through occupational practices. These various methods and opportunities are highlighted throughout issues of the newsletter.

In the August 1916 edition of *The Psychogram*, a patient using the pseudonym "Snapdragon" reflects on their experience working in the hospital's horticulture program. The horticulture and floriculture program at Greystone was one of the oldest established institutions at the hospital. Predating the arrival of medical director Evans in 1892, the primary form of occupational therapy was that of farm work and animal husbandry. A specific departmental school was established, which was conducted by the florist as the primary instructor, "where patients capable of becoming genuinely interested in the work receive attractive instruction in many branches of horticulture, floriculture, and the details of greenhouse work."[78]

According to the florist, his success lies in that he "strives to know each patient, does not expect to find any two alike, nor to interest and develop any two in precisely the same manner."[79] At the time of publication, patients working in the horticulture program at Greystone had grown nearly sixty thousand plants for both outdoor and indoor cultivation. She closes her piece reflecting that "to make this work successful both in the matter of production and the useful diversion and education of the patients, it is clearly essential that the Warden and Medical Director shall give their encouragement and support."[80] This program, which was facilitated with the help of the patients, received recognition from the public and press through honorary awards and coverage in local papers.[81]

---

[78] Snapdragon. *Floriculture at Greystone Park.* The Psychogram (Morris Plains), August 1916, 5.
[79] According to the June 1917 edition of The Psychogram the florist at Greystone Park was Otto Koch. Snapdragon. *Floriculture at Greystone Park.* The Psychogram (Morris Plains), August 1916, 5.
[80] Ibid.
[81] *Our Florist Commended.* The Psychogram (Morris Plains), June 1917, 7.

Patients often wrote poetry about events or activities they participated in or simply what they observed. One patient using the name "George A. Squire" wrote a poem about Greystone's gardens titled *The Flowers*. This was published in the March 1917 edition of The Psychogram:

> How wondrous are the flowers, that in one's garden grow. Their fragrance fills us with delight, their blow a beauty show.
> How come they there? From whence come they, or how or whom or why,
> Let's leave to Him who rules above, and not to you or I.[82]

The June 1917 edition of *The Psychogram* cited a report published by the New Jersey State Charities Aid and Prison Reform Association. In it the Association found that "in the many details of the florist's work there is much opportunity for occupational activity suitable for patients. In the laying out of flower beds on the lawns and in their care during the summer season the patients are benefited," that "more than all this is the value to the great mass of patients crowded on the wards in having in the corridors and in the dining halls a great abundance of cut flowers and blooming plants." On October 26, 1916 Greystone

---

[82] George A. Squire. *The Flowers.* The Psychogram (Morris Plains), March 1917, 17.

was awarded the certificate of merit by the Morris County

Gardeners and Florists' Society for its display of chrysanthemums,

chrysolora, and 20 blooms grown by Koch.[83]

Image 6: "Patients Engaged In Willow Culture" (Photo Courtesy of the Morris Plains Museum)

The expansive property grounds were farmed for

decorative plants as well those that had practical purposes. The

hospital was self-sufficient thanks to the assistance of the patients

employed in the occupational programs. Residents at institutions

often did work to help support the institution. Grob notes that

"most institutions attempted to offset the disorganization and

---

[83] *Our Florist Commended.* The Psychogram (Morris Plains), June 1917, 7.

monotony of hospital life by employing patients. Work was regarded as a critical element in creating a therapeutic environment. Inaction was considered harmful even to the normal mind, according to most psychiatrists, and in mental ill persons its results were devastating."[84]

An editor of The Psychogram reflected in the May 1917 edition that "all forms of employment used are selected with the purpose of helping those who take part in them and if possible also to make articles that can be used in the institution or on the grounds."[85] One of these practical applications was the cultivation of osiers, or willow shoots used in making baskets of different shapes and sizes.

It is noted in the May 1917 edition of *The Psychogram* that a number of patients were constantly repairing or making new baskets out of this material, so that it is now a business of itself. Five acres had been designated for the cultivation of osiers. Patients engaged in the part of the Industrial Division determined which shape and size is best fitted to the various baskets that are

---

[84] Grob, Gerald N. *Mental Illness and American Society: 1875-1940*. Princeton, NJ: Princeton University Press, 1983, 23.
[85] *Greystone's Osiery*. The Psychogram (Morris Plains), May 1917, 8.

required. These include waste paper baskets, laundry baskets and those used on the farm and in the gardens. In 1917 alone nearly three million osiers were harvested and were set aside to be used for the following year.[86]

Image 7: Farming at Greystone (Photo Courtesy of the Morris Plains Museum)

Without the contributions from the patients the hospital could not have been able to function. It was a city within itself. In most departments outside those in medical divisions the labor was conducted primarily in collaboration with patients. Patients could be found working in the Print Shop on The Psychogram, in the

---

[86] *Greystone's Osiery.* The Psychogram (Morris Plains), May 1917, 8.

Willow Holt cultivating osiers, in the cow barn and hennery managing livestock and collecting product. In addition, patients even helped to construct many buildings on the hospital campus. There was a carpentry shop, painting department, engineering department, and tailoring department. Patients also had opportunities to work within the firehouse, which was on hospital grounds.[87]

Hydrotherapy

The various therapeutic treatments that were available for patients at Greystone Park are detailed throughout The Psychogram's entire print run. These articles were primarily written by staff, however patients occasionally reflected on their experiences through letters that were published in the newsletter, as well as their extensive poetry contributions. These articles on the therapies that Greystone provided convey to the reader both how the hospital wanted to portray itself as a center of medical innovation and individualization, as well as lift a veil for the

---

[87] *Activities of the Current Month in the Various Departments of the Hospital.* The Psychogram (Morris Plains), May 1920, 10-11.

families that were concerned about how patients were being treated.

The use of water as a form of therapy can be traced back for centuries. During the early 20th century practitioners of hydrotherapy were beginning to develop an organized system with those specializing in this medium. Hydrotherapy includes the application of water in any form both internally and externally to treat a range of conditions, physical or mental. In the August 1916 edition of The Psychogram Dr. L.K. Henschel discusses how hydrotherapy was implemented at Greystone.[88]

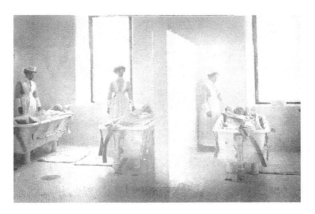

Image 8: Nurses Administering Continuous Baths, Psychogram, July 1925

(Courtesy of the Morris Plains Museum)

---

[88] Henschel, L.K. *Hydrotherapy for Mental and Nervous Diseases.* The Psychogram (Morris Plains), May 1917, 10.

Greystone had its own hydrotherapeutic department, which consisted of a washroom, a massage room, a wet pack room, and three dressing rooms. Nurses were in charge of the hydrotherapy room's continuous baths. Henschel reflects that hydrotherapy has had a significant impact on patient health, noting that "it has been found that patients who are depressed often improve rapidly under a course of hydrotherapeutic treatment." He also discusses how patients that are suffering from cardio-renal vascular diseases often benefit from hydrotherapeutic treatment. At Greystone the use of a wet pack was also used for treating excited and violent patients. Henschel explains that first the patient is "wrapped in a number of wet sheets pinned together by large safety pins or sewed together as some nurses prefer. On the patient's head is placed a compress made of towels which are kept wet with cold water."[89]

Nurses were given specific rules for the application of the continuous baths. The rules are as follows:

[89] Henschel, L.K. *Hydrotherapy for Mental and Nervous Diseases.* The Psychogram (Morris Plains), May 1917, 10.

1. When patient is brought to the continuous bath room the temperature, pulse and respiration are to be taken and charted.

2. The temperature of the water is never to be higher than 98 degrees.

3. No restraint of any kind is to be used on the patient while in the tub.

4. At 12 noon and 4PM temperature, pule and respiration are to be taken and charted.

5. Feeding: At 10AM and 4PM milk or egg nog. At dinner time patient may be removed from the tub for one and a half hours and given regular diet, unless the attending physician gives other orders.

6. Keep a record on the chart of how the patient reacts to the bath, noting the condition of the skin, how the patient sleeps and what conversation the patient carries on.[90]

---

[90] Ibid, 10.

Electrotherapy

In addition to hydrotherapy, Greystone maintained an

extensive electrotherapeutic department. In the January 1917

edition of The Psychogram Dr. Luis K. Henschel describes the

electrotherapeutic offerings of Greystone for patients with mental

illnesses. The first piece of equipment for electrotherapy was the

Holtz Electrostatic Machine. At the time it was a cutting-edge

piece of equipment. The model that was used at Greystone was

custom-made and located in the center of the Administration

Building. Due to its placement it was accessible from all parts of

the hospital for staff that needed to conduct electrotherapeutic

work. With this piece of equipment doctors were "equipped to do

throat and nose work, urethroscopy, endoscopy, and to use

Faradism and Galvanism when required."[91]

---

[91] Fardic and Galvanic currents were primarily used for diagnostic purposes and in the   treatment of organic nerve problems.
Henschel, L.K. *Electrotherapeutics in State Hospitals.* The Psychogram (Morris Plains), January 1917, 10.

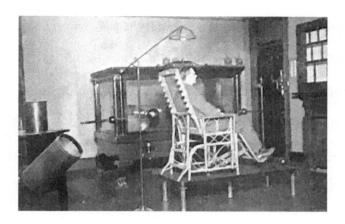

Image 9: Patient Receiving Static Breeze, Psychogram, January 1917

(Courtesy of the Morris Plains Museum)

Static breeze was also used as a form of electrotherapy. Static electricity was applied to the patient's head through the use of a highly-conductive non-contacting crown. This was used to "treat" many conditions, from treating headaches to being "quite efficacious in lowering blood pressure and inducing sleep," and Henschel notes that "the aim of the physician is to bring about sleep by natural methods instead of by drug medication, and the static breeze has been of considerable benefit along those lines."[92] Under Dr. Evans there was the underlying belief that the use of drugs should be limited, as they can easily be abused or

---

[92] Ibid, 11.

overprescribed. An alternative such as the static machine was an example of this underlying philosophy. Grob reflects that some psychiatrists were attracted to electrotherapy as many faced issues with the use of insulin and Metrazol therapy, which required specially trained physicians and nurses and frequently caused injuries to patients.[93]

The last major piece of medical equipment found in the electrotherapeutic department was the X-ray machine.[94] After petitioning to the governor and New Jersey Legislature for several years, Dr. Evans had obtained a fund in 1917 of $3,500 for the purchase of the machine. This machine provided staff with the ability to take pictures "of the head of each patient admitted, and in that way ascertain whether injuries to the skull, years previous have any bearing upon the patients' present mental illness." In addition, it was used to take pictures of a the patients' chests in order to diagnose pulmonary tuberculosis.[95]

---

[93] Grob, Gerald N. *Mental Illness and American Society: 1875-1940*. Princeton, NJ: Princeton University Press, 1983, 304
[94] According to the 1917 Annual Report of the Board of Managers and Officers of the New Jersey State Hospital at Morris Plains at the end of 1917 a new X-ray and electrotherapeutic outfit would be installed which replaced the static machine.
[95] Ibid, 11.

Entertainment as Therapy

In October of 1916 New Jersey Governor James Fielder visited Greystone Park to view the hospital grounds. He was given a tour by Dr. Evans. During his visit one of the focal points of conversation was the importance of providing "amusements" for the patients as a form of therapy. One of these forms of entertainment discussed was that of music therapy. Evans told the Governor that the "Monday night dances at the hospital had become such an established custom that they are one of the prerogatives of which the patients deem they should never be deprived."[96] Evans and others on his staff, such as Dr. Henschel, believed that the dances provided a distraction for patients to distance themselves from "brooding over imaginary troubles or worrying over financial and family affairs which cannot be remedied by worry."[97]

A female patient in the women's department told Dr. Henschel that the first dance she had since her wedding day was after her admission to the hospital for treatment, and how much

---

[96] Henschel, L.K. *Music and its Value in the Treatment of the Insane.* The Psychogram (Morris Plains), October 1916, 14.
[97] Ibid.

better she felt after listening to the orchestra and dancing for a couple of hours. Events such as the dances were a notable means of motivating patients to stay in line. They helped to reduce the amount of clothing and furniture that tended to be damaged during periods of outbursts. Those that were not on their best behavior were not allowed to attend. The orchestra that the patient enjoyed was composed of mainly male attendants and several male patients that had experience in theatrical orchestras. Every other Friday evening there was a dance followed by a film shown.[98]

Athletics was a major component of therapy at Greystone, as well as one of the most popular topics of conversation in The Psychogram. Greystone had several different sports teams composed of staff members as well as patients. The most popular were the baseball, bowling, and golf teams. Greystone had multiple baseball teams, all under the direction of physical director W. Moran. These teams were comprised of people from the various departments of the hospital. The print shop had their own team, as did the clinic. One team went by the name of the "soldiers," and another the "All-Stars," which consisted of the 9

---

[98] Ibid.

68

most proficient players from each team. As per the 1924 edition of the Psychogram, games were held on Monday, Wednesday, and Friday afternoons. According to a patient using the name "The Cub," the patients playing were "receiving the very best of coaching in the different ways of handling a ball, and especially are they instructed in the different ways of stopping those fast grounders that are sure to come every infielder's way."[99]

The highlight of all sporting events at Greystone, which in many cases received articles spanning several editions, were field days. The hospital held a field day each year. Dr. George R. Murray, who worked with patients in the gymnasium, noted the benefits of physical activity for patients. They not only helped the body, but directed the mind from ill thoughts or intentions. He reflected in the February 1917 edition of The Psychogram that the "value of a properly equipped gymnasium, under the direction of competent officials is not to be overestimated," that "many forms of insanity are the direct or indirect result of ill health due to lack of proper physical development."[100] Making physical activity

---

[99] The Cub. *Patient's Baseball League.* The Psychogram (Morris Plains), July 1924, 14.
[100] Murray, George R. *All State Hospitals Should be Equipped with Gymnasiums.* The Psychogram (Morris Plains), February 1917, 8.

enjoyable, as well as competitive, motivated patients to engage in this beneficial activity of their own will without the push of hospital staff.

Holidays at the Hospital

The holidays at Greystone were made by the staff to be a joyous occasion at the hospital. Staff presented patients with gifts and families could come to visit. Dr. Evans made his yearly appearance as Santa Claus for the patients as staff entertained the patients with games, music, and films. One patient, using the name "J.L.A.," reflected on his observations of the hospital holiday preparations that "every facility at their disposal will be taxed to the utmost in order that some additional rays of sunshine may penetrate thereby the lives of those entrusted to their care, and to the most of whom it comes as a rare occurrence."[101] Dr. George R. Hampton claimed that preparations for the celebration took four weeks. In the evening the hospital provided patients with a turkey dinner that Hampton noted could "compare favorably with that

---

[101] J.L.A. *Christmas at Greystone Park.* The Psychogram (Morris Plains), December 1916, 5.

served in ay first class hotel or private dwelling."[102] Another

patient, "The Colonel," appreciated the effort that went into

providing patients with a wholesome celebration:

> The aim of all appeared to entertain and instruct the
> patients, and in the endeavor everyone in any way
> connected with the management of the institution, from
> Medical Director Evans down to the most subordinate
> employee, seemed to take a hand, with credit to
> themselves and profit to those of us into whose lives they
> sought to inject a little sunshine.[103]

Image 10: "Dr. Evans as Santa Claus, 1916"

(Courtesy of the Morris Plains Museum)

---

[102] Hampton, George R. *Our Christmas Dinner.* The Psychogram (Morris Plains),
December 1916, 10.
[103] The Colonel. *The Holidays at the Hospital.* The Psychogram (Morris Plains),
January 1917, 4.

Personalizing Patient Care

Hospitals during the late 19th century and into the early 20th century were facing staffing shortages due to new nursing school graduates moving out of state for higher pay, as well as difficulty meeting the demand of the ever-increasing overcrowding. On October 30, 1894 Evans formed what became the Nurses and Attendants Training Program. According to Evans it was not a luxury, but a necessity. In the 1894 Annual Report for the hospital Evans reflected that "the practicability of training schools for nurses and attendants in an institution for the insane has been so clearly demonstrated in a number of hospitals in the country that the question does not admit an argument."[104]

The students at the training school were thrown into the fire and gained firsthand experience as scarlet fever broke out in the wards on February 4th, 1898. Lectures were suspended until the outbreak could be contained and attended to. This was another test many of the incoming nurses had to face in order to meet the

---

[104] Evans, Britton D. *"Annual Report of the Board of Managers of the New Jersey State Hospital at Morristown for the Year ending in October 31, 1894"* (Trenton, 1894), 103.

72

high standards that Evans held them to.[105] Evans notes in his

Annual Report of 1898 that this breakout caused much anxiety as

the virus is highly contagious. The first staff member of the

hospital to become ill was a male attendant. His room and the

entire ward he was assigned to were disinfected. It was believed

that the contagion had been eradicated, until fourteen days later

when a nurse noticed a rash forming on one of her patients as she

was conducting an examination.

Under Evans additions had been made to the hospital,

including what was known as the isolation cottage. This was a

separate building located a mile away from the main campus

buildings for the purpose of quarantining patients with contagious

diseases. Its sole form of communication was a telephone that was

connected to the main building. Evans recorded that the "total

number of cases was limited to 11, of which 8 were insane

patients, 2 were female nurses, 1 male attendant, and 1 a child in

the family of the florist."[106] Evans noted that everything had to be

---

[105] Evans, Britton D. "*Annual Report of the Board of Managers of the New Jersey State Hospital at Morristown for the Year ending in October 31, 1898*" (Trenton, 1898), 32.
[106] Evans, Britton D. "*Annual Report of the Board of Managers of the New Jersey State Hospital at Morristown for the Year ending in October 31, 1898*" (Trenton, 1898), 29.

disinfected, "the ceilings, walls, woodwork and furniture were washed with a string solution of bichloride of mercury. The rooms were then sealed, filled with formic aldehyde gas and kept closed for ten hours. The patients were given a bichloride bath and supplied with a change of sterile clothing."[107] No fatalities occurred during the outbreak.

Evans wanted Greystone to be holistic and objective in its hiring of nurses for the hospital. He did not want to follow the structures of other hospitals that fell to external pressures and internal politics. In terms of employing nurses Evans stated in his 1894 annual report that "selection will be made upon the intelligence, the moral character, the age, the general appearance and health of the candidate (…), and that "I shall observe strictly the principle that no preference shall be given to any special religious creed or the representatives of any particular political faith."[108] Men attended the nursing training school as well, but were called attendants. Nurses trained at the hospital were encouraged to apply for positions at Greystone, as they had the

---

[107] Ibid, 30.
[108] Evans, Britton D. *"Annual Report of the Board of Managers of the New Jersey State Hospital at Morristown for the Year ending in October 31, 1894"* (Trenton, 1894), 103.

advantage of working within the wards in which they gained their experience. As long as there were no conflicts, if you graduated from the nursing program you were guaranteed employment at the hospital. In addition, they met the expectations of the hospital administration as they were educated on site.[109]

Not everyone stayed at the hospital after graduation. In 1898 eleven women and two men who graduated from Greystone went on to serve at hospitals for the United States Army Camps. Evans noted that "telegrams were received from Surgeon-General Sternberg and Dr. Anita Newcomb McGee, expressing their appreciation to the hospital for furnishing these nurses when they were so urgently needed."[110]

The program was highly structured and included practical training for nurses, as well as traditional lecture-style of instruction. According to the October 1916 edition of *The Psychogram*, nurses graduated after three years in the program. There was textbook work and bi-weekly lectures, as well as practical application of their learned skills while working in the

---

[109] Ibid.
[110] Evans, Britton D. "*Annual Report of the Board of Managers of the New Jersey State Hospital at Morristown for the Year ending in October 31, 1898*" (Trenton, 1898), 33.

wards. The *Psychogram* details the curriculum covered in the

training school. The first year for students covered lectures on the

qualifications of a nurse, hygiene and diversional occupation,

anatomy, physiology, chemistry, physics, and dietetics. The

second and third year consisted of nervous and mental diseases,

dietetics, materia medica, medicine, surgery, pathology and

bacteriology. There were twenty-four lectures in total, with Evans

himself teaching several classes. During each year of study there

were comprehensive examinations that needed to be passed to

move forward in the program. During the first year of study there

were two examinations, and during the second and third year there

were eight examinations. Everything was completed within the

walls of the hospital.[111]

On June 3, 1907, Evans was the commencement speaker

for the graduating class of the Philadelphia School for Nurses.

This address was printed for the ceremony to be distributed to

attendants. In this commencement address Evans praised nurses

for their work, while also noting the seriousness of the role

professionalism and ethics plays in their profession. He declared

---

[111] Evans, Britton D. "Training School for Nurses." *The Psychogram* (Morris
Plains), October 1916, Vol. 1 ed., No. 4, 7.

that "the profession of nursing is a noble one, and while on its highest plane it must command respect; but its greatest success and fullest honors can best be attained by a strict observance of those proprieties and restraints which made its early existence possible."[112]

One of the themes throughout his speech is that of loyalty. Loyalty to the physician and loyalty to the profession. Evans had experience in the past with nurses that attempted to work outside their trained limits and he took these breaches of protocol with the utmost seriousness. He comments that nurses should "do nothing that suggests disloyalty to the physician, or that is calculated to cause a feeling of unrest or lack of confidence on the part of the family or the patient." He later declares that "(...) the duties of the nurse are very different from the duties of the physician, and that while the work of both the physician and nurse looks to the saving of life and restoration of the sick to health, the nurse must necessarily rely upon the physician for directions and that the

---

[112] Evans, Britton D. *The Nurse and Her Mission*. Philadelphia, PA: Philadelphia School for Nurses, 1908, 7.

physician must, on the other hand, repose much confidence in the nurse."[113]

A final concern that Evans shared with the graduating class of nurses was that of drug dependence. He reflected that he has seen nurses that became dependent on drugs as they felt obligated to remain at the bedsides of their patients for as long a duration as possible, however this "often leads her to take powerful medicinal agents with consequences disastrous to herself." The drug in particular Evans is referencing is "the seductive alkaloid of opium-morphine." He commented that "I have seen the lives of some of the brightest, most intelligent and capable nurses blighted by the use of this drug (...)." He warned them to be careful when prescribing dangerous painkillers such as morphine, as well as not to abuse the drug themselves. He stated "they who use the hypodermic shall perish by the hypodermic."[114]

---

[113] Evans, Britton D. *The Nurse and Her Mission*. Philadelphia, PA: Philadelphia School for Nurses, 1908, 8, 15.
[114] Evans, Britton D. *The Nurse and Her Mission*. Philadelphia, PA: Philadelphia School for Nurses, 1908, 25-26.

Image 11: Graduating Class of Nurses, 1902. (Courtesy of the Morris Plains Museum)

Evans had five main qualifications in order for someone to be hired as a nurse at Greystone. They are as follows:

1. Sufficient education and intelligence to take the course of training.

2. Good health.

3. Good more character and sobriety.

4. Musical ability and experience in athletics sufficient to assist in orchestra, band, choir and outdoor amusements.

5. Industry and kind-heartedness. [115]

---

[115] Evans, Britton D. *"Annual Report of the Board of Managers of the New Jersey State Hospital at Morristown for the Year ending in October 31, 1898"* (Trenton, 1898), 33.

Conclusion

In conclusion, *The Psychogram* newsletter was the unique product of a collaborative process between medical staff and patients. It provided patients with an outlet to voice their insights into the workings of a psychiatric hospital during the 20th century. In addition, the creation of the newsletter was a progressive form of treatment that enabled patients to develop the skills they needed once they were discharged in a setting that provided a sense of normalcy. Under the leadership of administrators, such as Dr. Britton Evans, staff at Greystone Park Psychiatric Hospital structured and implemented a comprehensive occupation therapy program for patients of which *The Psychogram* was an essential component. Having therapeutic programs such as the production of a hospital newsletter helped to set Greystone apart from other hospitals in New Jersey at a time when issues such as overcrowding plagued institutions.

Nurses played a crucial role in facilitating the programs that mental hospitals such as Greystone established. In 1884 Dr. Evans established his training school for nurses at Greystone. As a result, nurses at Greystone received specialized training that best equipped them to provide patients with personalized care as they administered or facilitated a variety of therapies. Without the aid of nurses at the hospital occupational therapy programs such as *The Psychogram* would not have been feasible.

CHAPTER 4

LEADING THE WAY

On June 2nd, 1917 a banquet was held at the Robert Treat Hotel in Newark to honor Dr. Evans' 25 years of service to the hospital. Guests were present from every walk of life. There were those from the medical and legal field, as well as politicians. The Hon. Thomas J. Hillary, an ex-State Senator from Morris, said he had often come in touch with Doctor Evans while he was in the legislature, and that Evans over the years asked repeatedly for necessary appropriations for needed improvements. His accomplishments, such as the development of the occupational therapy program and Psychogram, were honored. The nurses and staff presented Evans with a diamond ring. State Senator James E. Martine noted Evans as a "model head of a model institution."[116]

To close the ceremony Evans reflected that "Those for whom I work are members of afflicted humanity who are unable to do anything for themselves, or ask for what they need, and it

---

[116] "Medical Director for Twenty-Five Years". *The Psychogram* (Morris Plains), June 1917, Vol. 1 ed., No. 12, 3.

becomes my duty on numerous occasions to ask for what they require…"[117] The devotion of Dr. Evans and his staff in using the latest medical treatments and therapies demonstrated their focus on patient care, which continued throughout the 20th century.

In July of 1920 Greystone hosted an exhibition of the work done by patients in the occupational therapy program. The exhibits included printed products, such as ledgers, day books, and record books. Products from both the Men's and Women's Arts and Crafts Departments included baskets woven from the willows, brushes, brooms, and raffia work. However, the most significant item on display was the collection of Psychogram issues.[118]

Anniversary celebrations continued years later. July 3rd, 1940 marked the 24th anniversary of the first issue of The Psychogram. To acknowledge the significance of this landmark anniversary the Morris Plains Chronicle published an article titled "Greystone Magazine Has Birthday." They note that it became "accepted throughout the world as one of the great advances in occupational therapy," that it was a product of "long, consideration and much discussion by the medical staff, the idea

---

[117] Ibid.
[118] "Greystone Park to Exhibit." *The Chatham Press*. July 31, 1920.

83

was put into practice in the belief that it could open the road to self-expression by those intellectually inclined and provide steady, pleasant work and better health for any others under the care of the institution."[119] The newsletter was written and printed at Greystone, and included in its pages advertisements for local businesses. Promotions ranged from publishers, car dealerships, to exterminators, as well as jewelers. Greystone was a landmark in Morris Plains, and *The Psychogram* was in many ways a community publication.

---

[119] "Greystone Magazine Has Birthday." *Morris County Chronicle,* July 3, 1940.

Reflections

As Greystone continued to grow[120] and patients came and went *The Psychogram* endured as a time capsule of the experiences and psyche of those that were a part of this unique community. It was a community in which both patients and staff collaborated to produce works of literature and prose that are enduring and provide unique insights into their lives. Poetry was a means through which patients channeled their anxiety, depression, and hopes in order to normalize and reflect on the situation in which they had been placed.

Poetry was usually given its own page in *The Psychogram*. The title of the section was "Original Poems by Patients." The three main themes that permeate the poems of *The Psychogram* were loss, love, and faith. However, poems could also be found throughout the newsletter, in many instances without any specific significance for placement. Some recurrent patient authors, such as Prince Michael of Saxony, were given their own

---

[120] The annual reports of the hospital record this dramatic increase in patients residing at the hospital. In 1910 there were 2,118 patients, in 1920, 2,713, and in 1940 there were 6,195.

separate page, as well as multi-part pieces that were serialized throughout multiple issues of the newsletter.

In the early editions of the newsletter a frequent topic of discussion was war, in particular World War One. According to Daniel Myers, curator of the Morris Plains museum, not all workers at Greystone were there as mental patients. Some were conscientious objectors and were relegated to provide labor at Greystone. These objectors may have been employed within the print shop of the men's Industrial Building. Throughout both World Wars the newsletter featured a page or more to what was happening abroad, as well as listed staff members that withdrew from the hospital to respond to their country's call.[121] Reflecting that patients at the hospital were not shielded from the emotional toll that war inflicted on families, a patient using the pseudonym "Mrs. A. McG." wrote:

Grief

A little word may strength impart,
And give fresh courage to the heart,
May soothe a smart and ease a pain,
And bring back joy and peace again.

---

[121] Sullivan, Nathaniel. "Interview of Daniel Myers." 19 Sep. 2019.

A word in season whispered low,
In friendly tone may banish woe,
May calm the tumult in the breast,
And lull each care and grief to rest.

Oh! Could we know the subtle power,
Of one kind word in sorrow's hour,
Then would we know the heart's relief,
When sunlight breaks the clouds of grief.[122]

"Grief" fully displays the sense of hopelessness that permeated the minds of many Americans. Another poem that reflects another perspective at the hospital during the First World War is by a patient using the pseudonym R.W.E. Titled "Love and Peace," they wrote:

This nation wants no wound,
Our country's heart is sound,

Let us have patience, peace;
We pray that war shall cease.
We want no war or foe,
No battle ground or woe,
But consecrate to Thee,
And all in Christ be free.

To do our best each day,

In life to love His way,

For right is God indeed,
When all souls Christ they heed.[123]

---

[122] McG., Mrs. A. *Grief*. The Psychogram (Morris Plains), August 1916, 7.
[123] R.W.E. *Love and Peace*. The Psychogram (Morris Plains), August 1916, 7.

R.W.E. demonstrates that not all patients staying at the hospital were in despair regarding the war, but held out hope. However, poems such as these were another unique insight, which provided the public with the diverse perspectives on the war that could be found within the hospital walls.

Years later, following the end of World War II, Greystone had several articles concerning the war, as well as employees that were called to serve. In the October 1945 edition of *The Psychogram* on the back of the cover page the editors listed all the hospital employees that served. Members of the staff that served came from all departments, including the Occupational Therapy Department.[124] Articles such as these may have helped to form a sense of community among the hospital community and that of Morris Plains.

Many of these poems bring to light the emotional turmoil that patients endured while staying at the hospital, separated from loved ones. One in particular, "Neglected – Not Understood"

---

[124] The Psychogram (Morris Plains), October 1945.

displays a sense of optimism that befell its author. Moncrieff

Montgomerie ends his poem with these lines:

> How many lonely, cheerless hearts are aching.
> For lack of sympathy-Ah! Day by day,
> How many fond and loving hearts are breaking,
> Dragging noble spirits, men and women, hence away.
> Neglected – misunderstood.
>
> Oh, God! That all might see a little clearer,
> Or judge more justly – when they cannot see.
> Oh, God! Help to draw a little nearer.
> One another – then they'll be nearer Thee.
> And understand – be understood.[125]

Prince Michael of Saxony, known for his short stories and articles

in *The Psychogram,* contributed a poem of his own that shares this

sentiment of loss, as well as separation. His poem, titled "To M.,

Duchess of L," reads as follows:

> Ever I seek the lost love of my soul,
> This is my soul-life. This is its goal,
> Ever she hideth herself from my eyes,
> Why she so hideth, I know not, nor care,
> All that I want, is to kiss her dark hair,
> All that I want, is to view her loved eyes,
> All that I have, will I give as a prize
> To him who will show me the place where she lies.[126]

---

[125] Montgomerie, Moncrieff. *Neglected – Not Understood.* The Psychogram (Morris Plains), January 1917, 13.
[126] Prince Michael of Saxony. *To M., Duchess of L.* The Psychogram (Morris Plains), January 1917, 13.

In 1930 Richard David Comstock, a former patient and editor of *The Psychogram,* published *Rhymes of a Raver.* This book details his life prior to, during, and after residing at Greystone. Deeming himself a cowboy, fire fighter, as well as a horticulturalist, Comstock walks the reader down the path of his successes and failures. Alcohol brought him to his lowest point in life, "in the gutter." Comstock gives a considerable amount of gratitude to the staff of Greystone. He reflects that "Greystone Park may well be christened a Castle of Salvaged Souls. For so often here an almost new body must be builded around an undeveloped spirit ere it reaches the realization that a soul is existent. And it seems to me that it is only fair to those of Greystone Park for me to state plainly that it was here that I found I had a soul and could ever hope to lead a happy, useful, contented life, rebuilt in mind and body."[127]

Many former patients became subscribers of *The Psychogram*. This provided them with the opportunity to stay updated with what was occurring at the hospital. In addition, some wrote to the newsletter to update patients on their lives after

---

[127] Comstock, Richard David. *Rhymes of a Raver: Tribute to a Castle of Salvaged Souls,* 2016.

institutionalization and to give them hope. A letter from Alice G. Loux was published in the February 1917 edition of *The Psychogram*. In it she reminisces about her time at Greystone and how the newsletter's "illuminations and familiar names revived memories of my stay there." She reflects on the diversity of the patients present at the hospital. She notes that she knew patients from states as far away as Texas and California, as well as countries such as France, Italy, Germany, Switzerland, Norway, England, and Ireland. Commenting on her time at Greystone, Alice remarked that "There is monotony, and yet things do not stand still, there are frequent comings and goings; persons that touch our lives, then pass on leaving relief, or regret, in the hearts of those who remain."[128]

Like Alice, patients often wrote poems about the passage of time or general observations they made daily. Not all patients were released from Greystone. Many were there for the rest of their lives. Having the opportunity to creatively express themselves, such as in the form of poetry contributions, provided

---

[128] Loux, Alice G. *A Letter from a Former Patient*. The Psychogram (Morris Plains), February 1917, 7.

patients with a means to vent their emotions and reflect on their experiences.

The voices found in the pages of *The Psychogram* brought to light deep personal thoughts regarding isolation, depression, as well as separation from loved ones. The writings of the patients also brought insight into the more mundane passing thoughts patients had that may not have been charted if not for the production of this newsletter. One patient, unnamed, in the June 1917 edition of *The Psychogram wrote* a short passage titled "Indecision." They wrote:

> To be too bad to die, too good to do so, is it to be much like the doubting, hesitating, wavering man who said his shirt was too dirty to wear and not dirty enough to send to the laundry.[129]

This in-between state displayed within this poem encapsulates a feeling patients may have had of a loss of self-worth. While many poems were romantic and outlandish in nature, those such as "Indecision," express the feeling of a loss of soul, of having nothing to live for.

---

[129] *Indecision*. The Psychogram (Morris Plains), June 1917, 12.

Then and Now

On January 14th, 1920 Dr. Evans died from complications related to heart disease.[130] Although he died just four years after its initial publication, *The Psychogram* was published until 1977. According to Daniel Myers the decline of the newsletter began around the 1950s when the ACLU determined that any patient working in the occupational therapy program had to receive payment. [131]

Image 12: The August 1916 and Fall-Winter 1977 editions of The Psychogram.

(Courtesy of the Morris Plains Museum and Morristown Public Library)

---

[130] "Dr. B. D. Evans, Noted as Alienist, Is Dead." *The New York Times*, 15 Jan. 1920.
[131] Sullivan, Nathaniel. "Interview of Daniel Myers." 22 Jun. 2019.

By the late 1960s the condition of the hospital and quality

of care deteriorated. This was a reflection of the overall decline in

the mental health care system in the United States. Although many

social policies under Presidents John F., Kennedy and Lyndon B.

Johnson were passed, and additional funding was provided for the

mentally ill, Grob notes that events such as the war in Vietnam

had a negative, lasting impact on many of those domestic

initiatives. The funding promised to mental institutions was

substantially higher than what was actually received. Finally,

when Richard Nixon took office in 1969 the relationship between

the Executive Branch and the psychiatric community grew

tense.[132]

The landmark piece of legislation passed during this era

that failed to meet the needs of the mentally ill was the *Community

Mental Health Act*. Passed in 1963, President Kennedy remarked

on October 31st of that year that it would "expand our knowledge,

provide research facilities to determine the cause of retardation,

establish university related diagnostic treatment clinics and permit

the construction of community centers for the car of the

---

[132] Grob, Gerald N. *Mad Among Us*. Riverside: Free Press, 2011, 279-80.

retarded."[133] This law began the process of deinstitutionalization, which impacted large state-run mental asylums, such as Greystone, where the quality of care took a nosedive in the decades to follow.

Carole Golcher worked in Greystone's occupational therapy program from 1967 to 1970. The program at that time primarily consisted of arts and crafts. Patients were engaged in activities such as woodworking, ceramic, leatherwork, and weaving. Patients stayed for an hour daily. According to Carole, by the time of her arrival at Greystone the conditions were deplorable. She reflected that many of the patients "were delusional, hallucinating, and some were very spaced out due to medications." The hospital in her view during this period was a "snake pit."[134]

Carole worked with two different segments of the Greystone population during this time. First was the male population in the Main Building where patients of all ages were

---

[133] "Remarks on Signing Mental Retardation Facilities and Community Health Centers Construction Bill, 31 October 1963: JFK Library." Remarks on signing mental retardation facilities and community health centers construction bill, 31 October 1963 | JFK Library, October 31, 1963. https://www.jfklibrary.org/asset-viewer/archives/JFKPOF/047/JFKPOF-047-045.
[134] Sullivan, Nathaniel. "Interview of Carole Golcher." 8 March. 2020.

housed. Patients had varied forms of mental illness, but most suffered from different types of schizophrenia. Carole commented that most patients were actively hallucinating and suffering from paranoid thoughts and delusions.[135]

The occupational therapy program during her time at Greystone was headed by Lucille Boss and had registered occupational therapists on staff. Carole, along with other staff members in the occupational therapy department, had to go to the wards to collect the patients to bring them back to their workspace. She reflected that she never wanted to walk the wards alone, as it was too dangerous to do so. She noted that many wards were completely unattended by any staff at all.[136]

---

[135] Ibid.
[136] Ibid.

Conclusion

By the 1960s what used to be a monthly newsletter became a small pamphlet, which was issued quarterly. The April 1966 edition of *The Psychogram* was small both in size and content. Patient contributions were not included in any form. Whereas the earlier editions of the newsletter noted in bold text on the cover "Done once a month in the print shop of the New Jersey State Hospital at Morris Plains," these later editions stated "Published quarterly by the Medical Department of the New Jersey State Hospital at Greystone Park, New Jersey" above the table of contents.[137]

As the hospital could not afford to pay hundreds of patients for their labor the newsletter was left to the hospital staff to maintain. Contributions were from hospital staff and include contact information listings, a page with dates and hours for the post office, general visiting days, religious services, library hours, and movie times. There was a page dedicated to listing employee awards, as well as two separate pages with columns written by the hospital chaplains. The only mention of the Occupational Therapy

---

[137] Crandell, Archie. The Psychogram (Morris Plains), April 1966.

department is a small notice on the bottom of a page saying that articles produced by patients working in the Women's Arts and Crafts Building were available for purchase Mondays through Saturdays in a designated Sales Room.[138]

The charm that made the early editions was lost. Patient poems, letters, and articles were phased out and replaced with articles written by medical staff for medical staff. The later issues had an occasional article about the different departments and administrators in the hospital, however none included the viewpoints of patients.

The last edition of *The Psychogram* was published the in the winter of 1977. In it there is an article about the changing role of a hospital pharmacist, written by the pharmaceutical services supervisor and an article about dietitians, written by the Food Service Department. The final issue also included a "Greystone Welcomes" section, which detailed new administrative staff, with a photograph and small biographical summary. In contrast to the earlier editions that were large in size and page-length, the final issues were small and published only twice annually.[139]

---

[138] *Hospital Calendar.* The Psychogram (Morris Plains), April 1966, 4.
[139] Soloway, Richard T. The Psychogram (Morris Plains), 1977.

CHAPTER 5

CONCLUSION

By the turn of the twenty-first century *The Psychogram* was long gone, forgotten, and many buildings in the hospital complex were vacant and in need of major repairs. On July 26, 2008 the state opened a new Greystone Park Psychiatric Hospital. This hospital was within walking distance of the original hospital complex. More than 400 patients moved into the new facility. The total cost was $200 million. The new hospital is less than half the size of the original structure, at 450,000 square feet. Matt Rainey, reporter for *The Star-Ledger*, noted that:

> The new hospital replaces five aging treatment buildings and a nearly 132-year-old administration building. It is a 450-bed facility in a single, self-contained building that includes a treatment mall with over 21 rooms for various activities and a large auditorium, said state officials. In addition, there are also residential cottages for 60 additional patients, bringing the hospital's capacity to 510.[140]

---

[140] Ragonese, Lawrence. The Star-Ledger, "Greystone Park Psychiatric Hospital Opens after Months-Long Delay." *Nj*, 16 July 2008, www.nj.com/news/2008/07/the_new_170_million_greystone.html.

Image 13: Main Building, Greystone Park, June, 2015

In August of 2008 the New Jersey Department of the Treasury announced plans to demolish the Main Building and surrounding complex.[141] Multiple attempts by preservationists were made to save the original hospital architecture. One of the leading groups was *Preserve Greystone*, which held multiple protests and took legal action to stall the demolition.[142]

Another advocate for preservation was Nora Guthrie, the daughter of the folk-music icon. In the 1950s Woody Guthrie was not a psychiatric patient, but stayed at Greystone in Ward 40.

---

[141] Horowitz, Ben. "State Planning to Tear down Historic Main Building at Old Greystone Hospital." nj, August 18, 2013.
https://www.nj.com/morris/2013/08/state_planning_to_tear_down_historic_main_building_at_old_greystone_hospital.html.
[142] "Preserve Greystone - Home." Preserve Greystone - Home.
http://www.preservegreystone.org/.

There "was no better place for him to go" while suffering from Huntington's disease, Nora reflected in an article for NJ.com. In 2013 Nora Guthrie promoted the book *Woody Guthrie's Wardy Forty: Greystone Park State Hospital Revisited*," which details Guthrie's time at Greystone in the 1950s and features pictures taken inside the hospital, along with artifacts. Phillip Behler, the photographer and author, compared Greystone to Ellis Island, pointed out it opened "right after the Civil War," when "everybody became shell-shocked," which "represented an early recognition of what came to be known as post-traumatic stress disorder."[143]

In October of 2015 the NorthStar Contracting Group began the demolition of the main building structure. John Huebner, former president of Preserve Greystone, in an article for NJ.com reflected that "State and local officials had an opportunity to work with the private sector to do something really great and

---

[143] Horowitz, Ben. "Woody Guthrie's Daughter Wants to Preserve Greystone, Her Dad's Old Home." *Nj*, 26 Jan. 2014, www.nj.com/morris/2014/01/woody_guthries_daughter_wants_to_preserve_grey stone_woodys_home_for_5_years.html.

positive here." In addition, "This is a terrible waste of public money and property."[144]

From the arrival of Dr. Evans in 1892, Greystone Park Psychiatric Hospital went through a series of changes. The most significant was the expansion and standardization of the hospital's occupational therapy program. The centerpiece of this program was the production of *The Psychogram* newsletter, which ran from 1916-1977.

Hospital newsletters such as *The Psychogram* encapsulate progressive values that administrators and psychiatrists strove to achieve at a time in the early twentieth century when institutions were beginning to garner scrutiny from the public. While many hospitals had a form of occupational therapy, which were primarily manual labor, Greystone's program was substantial in its scope, size, and creative outlets. Rothman notes that while some hospitals utilized these programs for their economic benefit, to others, "occupational therapy represented an antidote to the fact

---

[144] Horowitz, Ben. "Final Demolition at Greystone Angers Preservation Leaders." nj, October 8, 2015.
https://www.nj.com/morris/2015/10/preservation_leaders_saddened_as_final_de molition.html.

that patients come to the mental hospital with a feeling of unreality," and that "work, and especially work in making something beautiful, seems real and is therefore one of the most useful means of combating some of the effects of the mental disorder."[145] The Psychogram provided therapeutic benefits for patients, however it also provided economic benefits for the hospital. Within the pages of the newsletter, doctors and staff were able to market the hospital as a center of innovation through the inclusion of articles related to treatments. In almost every issue there was a notice related to events held on the hospital grounds that the public could attend or market days where visitors could purchase wares made by patients. In addition, local businesses could pay to include advertisements in the last two or three pages of every edition.

Hospital newsletters, such as *The Psychogram,* helped to dispel negative misconceptions that families had regarding the treatment of the mentally ill within an institutional setting. Our historical understanding of mental institutions would not be complete without studying *The Psychogram*. It provides historians

---

[145] Rothman, David J. *Conscience and Convenience: the Asylum and Its Alternatives in Progressive America*. Routledge, 2017, 345.

with a unique insight into the workings of a psychiatric hospital from the perspective of patients and their understanding of their treatment. Lastly, *The Psychogram* endures as a model of a unique and successful form of occupational therapy that can be replicated today. Although Greystone has been demolished and its grounds reshaped, the voices of those thousands of patients that walked the halls of the hospital live on within the pages of *The Psychogram*.

Institutions such as prisons and mental hospitals today can look at newsletters such as *The Psychogram* for inspiration to emulate. Institutions can publish print newsletters or moderated websites with input from prisoners or patients. Occupational therapy programs can still benefit from creative outlets such as communal publications like a newsletter to bridge the staff-patient divide and prepare individuals for life outside the institution. *The Psychogram* can be a starting point for historians studying institutions of the past. Much can be learned about mental hospitals and other institutional settings when the focus is redirected away from administration and towards the patients. Creative output from patients, whether it is artwork, poetry, or letters can provide scholars with a unique perspective which could alter preconceptions about treatment and daily hospital life.

Image 14: The Former Location of

Greystone Park Psychiatric Hospital

BIBLIOGRAPHY

Primary Sources

"State Hospital Inmates Enter Newspaper Field." *The Central New Jersey Home News*. March 27, 1917

"Greystone Park to Exhibit." *The Chatham Press*. July 31, 1920

Crandell, Archie. The Psychogram (Morris Plains), April 1966

Curry, M. A. The Psychogram (Morris Plains), July 1924

Curry, M. A. The Psychogram (Morris Plains), October 1945

Evans, Britton D. The Psychogram (Morris Plains), August 1916

Evans, Britton D. The Psychogram (Morris Plains), December 1916

Evans, Britton D. The Psychogram (Morris Plains), January 1917

Evans, Britton D. The Psychogram (Morris Plains), February 1917

Evans, Britton D. The Psychogram (Morris Plains), March 1917

Evans, Britton D. The Psychogram (Morris Plains), May 1917

Evans, Britton D. The Psychogram (Morris Plains), June 1917

Evans, Britton D. The Psychogram (Morris Plains), May 1920

Evans, Britton D. *"Annual Report of the Board of Managers of the New Jersey State Hospital at Morristown for the Year ending in October 31, 1892"* (Trenton, 1894)

Evans, Britton D. *"Annual Report of the Board of Managers of the New Jersey State Hospital at Morristown for the Year ending in October 31, 1898"* (Trenton, 1898)

"The N.J. State Hospital. Something About This Great Institution at Morris Plains - B. D. Evans, Medical Director." *The Journal*, November 1894

Evans, Britton D. "Training School for Nurses." *The Psychogram* (Morris Plains), October 1916, Vol. 1 ed., No. 4

Evans, Britton D. "Institutional Care of the Insane." *Journal of The Medical Society of New Jersey* XIII, no. 1 (January 1916): 1–6

Evans, Britton D. "History of the New Jersey State Hospital at Morris Plains" *The Psychogram* (Morris Plains), November 1916

Evans, Britton D. *The Nurse and Her Mission*. Philadelphia, PA: Philadelphia School for Nurses, 1908

Evans, Britton D., and Frank M. Mikels. "*The Therapeutic and Economic Value of Diversional Occupation.*" The American Journal of Insanity LXXII (1915)

Evans, Britton D. "*Annual Report of the Board of Managers of the New Jersey State Hospital at Morristown for the Year ending in October 31, 1902*" (Morris Plains)

Evans, Britton D. "*Annual Report of the Board of Managers of the New Jersey State Hospital at Morristown for the Year ending in October 31, 1914*" (Trenton, 1894),

Evans, Britton D. "*Annual Report of the Board of Managers of the New Jersey State Hospital at Morristown For the Period From November 1st 1917 to June 30th 1918*" (Hospital Print, 1919)

Fisher, E. Moore "History of the New Jersey State Hospital at Morris Plains" The Psychogram (Morris Plains), October 1916

Hampton, George R. "Modern Care of the Insane." *The Psychogram* (Morris Plains), February 1917

Henschel, L.K. *Music and its Value in the Treatment of the Insane.* The Psychogram (Morris Plains), October 1916

Henschel, L.K. *Electrotherapeutics in State Hospitals.* The Psychogram (Morris Plains), January 1917

Henschel, L.K. *Hydrotherapy for Mental and Nervous Diseases.* The Psychogram (Morris Plains), May 1917

Horowitz, Ben. "State Planning to Tear down Historic Main Building at Old Greystone Hospital." nj, August 18, 2013. https://www.nj.com/morris/2013/08/state_planning_to_tear_down_historic_main_building_at_old_greystone_hospital.html.

Horowitz, Ben. "Woody Guthrie's Daughter Wants to Preserve Greystone, Her Dad's Old Home." *Nj*, 26 Jan. 2014, www.nj.com/morris/2014/01/woody_guthries_daughter_wants_to_preserve_greystone_woodys_home_for_5_years.html.

Horowitz, Ben. "Final Demolition at Greystone Angers Preservation Leaders." nj, October 8, 2015 https://www.nj.com/morris/2015/10/preservation_leaders_saddened_as_final_demolition.html.

Mikels, Frank M. "Diversional Occupation for Patients." *The Psychogram* (Morris Plains), November 1916, Vol. 1 ed., No. 5

"Greystone Magazine Has Birthday." *Morris County Chronicle,* July 3, 1940

"The State and Its Insane." *Newark Daily Advertiser.* December 7, 1894

"Dr. B. D. Evans, Noted as Alienist, Is Dead." *The New York Times*, 15 Jan. 1920

Murray, George R. *All State Hospitals Should be Equipped with Gymnasiums.* The Psychogram (Morris Plains), February 1917.

Ragonese, Lawrence. The Star-Ledger, "Greystone Park Psychiatric Hospital Opens after Months-Long Delay." *Nj*, 16 July 2008, www.nj.com/news/2008/07/the_new_170_million_greystone.html.

Soloway, Richard T. The Psychogram (Morris Plains), 1977.

Stryker, Thomas J. *"1876 Annual Report of the Managers and Officers of the New Jersey State Lunatic Asylum at Trenton"* (Trenton, 1876)

Sullivan, Nathaniel. "Interview of Carole Golcher." 8 March. 2020

Sullivan, Nathaniel. "Interview of Daniel Myers." 19 Sep. 2019

Sullivan, Nathaniel. "Interview of Frank Rybasack." 15 Dec. 2019

Sullivan, Nathaniel. "Interview of Olin "Butch" Acker." 15 Dec. 2019

Secondary Sources

Anderson, Katherine. *Behind the Walls: Hidden Histories*, 2013, 8

Biographical and Genealogical History of Morris County, New Jersey, Volume I, the Lewis Publishing Company, New York and Chicago

Comstock, Richard David. *Rhymes of a Raver: Tribute to a Castle of Salvaged Souls*, 2016

Foucault, Michel. *Madness and Civilization: a History of Insanity in the Age of Reason*. New York, NY: Vintage Books, 1988

Goffman, Erving, *Asylums: Essays on the Social Situation of Mental Patients and Other Inmates* (New York, NY: Anchor, 1961)

Grob, Gerald N. *Mental Illness and American Society: 1875-1940*. Princeton, NJ: Princeton University Press, 1983

Grob, Gerald N. *Mad Among Us*. Riverside: Free Press, 2011

Gollaher, David. *Voice for the Mad: The Life of Dorothea Dix*. New York: Free Press, 1995

Katz, Michael B. *In the Shadow of the Poorhouse a Social History of Welfare in America*. New York: BasicBooks, 1998

"Time Line." Preserve Greystone - History of Greystone Park Psychiatric Hospital. http://preservegreystone.org/history.html

Prior, Pauline, and Gillian Mcclelland. "Through the Lens of the Hospital Magazine: Downshire and Holywell Psychiatric Hospitals in the 1960s and 1970s." *History of Psychiatry* 24, no. 4 (2013): 399–414

"Remarks on Signing Mental Retardation Facilities and Community Health Centers Construction Bill, 31 October 1963: JFK Library." Remarks on signing mental retardation facilities and community health centers construction bill, 31 October 1963 | JFK Library, October 31, 1963. https://www.jfklibrary.org/asset-viewer/archives/JFKPOF/047/JFKPOF-047-045

Rothman, David J. *Conscience and Convenience: the Asylum and Its Alternatives in Progressive America*. Routledge, 2017

Reiss, Benjamin. *Theaters of Madness*. Chicago: University of Chicago Press, 2008

Scull, Andrew. *Madhouse: A Tragic Tale of Megalomania and Modern Medicine*. New Haven, Conn: Yale University Press, 2007

Smoyak, Shirley A. "What's New Is Really Old." *Journal of Psychosocial Nursing* 45, no. 10, 2007

Sutton, John R. "The Political Economy of Madness: The Expansion of the Asylum in Progressive America." *American Sociological Review* 56, no. 5 (1991)

Tagliareni, Rusty, and Christina Mathews. *Greystone Park Psychiatric Hospital*. Charleston, SC: Arcadia Publishing, 2016

CPSIA information can be obtained
at www.ICGtesting.com
Printed in the USA
BVHW090409160222
629082BV00012B/1040